# Engineering the Future:

## Science, Technology, and the Design Process

**National Center for
Technological Literacy**®

Museum of Science, Boston

**Key Curriculum Press
Emeryville, CA**

**Project Team**
**Key Curriculum Press**
Project Lead: Ladie Malek
Editorial Assistant: Christa Edwards
Production Director: Christine Osborne
Production Coordinator: Jennifer Young
Cover Designer: Jensen Barnes
Prepress and Printer: Versa Press

Textbook Product Manager: James Ryan
Publisher: Steven Rasmussen

Published by Key Curriculum Press.
© 2008 Museum of Science, Boston. All rights reserved.

Cover Photo Credit: PhotoDisc "Popular Objects" by Ryan McVay, PhotoDisc "Portfolio," PhotoDisc Volume 95 "Youth Culture," PhotoDisc Volume 4 "Science, Technology and Medicine" Version 2

*Engineering the Future: Science, Technology, and the Design Process* is a trademark of the National Center for Technological Literacy (NCTL) at the Museum of Science, Boston.

® Key Curriculum Press is a registered trademark of Key Curriculum Press. All other registered trademarks and trademarks in this book are the property of their respective holders.

Key Curriculum Press
1150 65th Street
Emeryville, CA 94608
editorial@keypress.com
www.keypress.com

Printed in the United States of America
10 9 8 7 6 5 4 3 2     10 09 08
ISBN: 978-1-55953-963-0

**Project Team**
**Museum of Science, Boston**
Project Director: Cary I. Sneider
Program Manager: Julie Brenninkmeyer
Curriculum Developers: Lee C. Pulis, Joel Rosenberg
Professional Development Content Developers: Johanna Bunn, Dan Tyman
Editor: Rebecca Pollard Pierik
Contributing Writers: Benjamin T. Erwin, Donald Foster, Chris Mrowka, John Ost,
Joel Rosenberg
Content Reviewers: Kate Bielaczyc, Beth Miaoulis, Nancy Schalch, George Taliadouros,
Laurette Viteritti, Camille Wainwright
Researchers: Kate Bielaczyc, Carol Symmons, Shih-Ying Yao
Assistants: Heather Hathaway, Katy Capo
Artist and Designer: Braden Chang
Production Services: Publishing Solutions Group, Inc.


President of the Museum of Science and Director of the NCTL: Ioannis (Yannis) M. Miaoulis
Associate Director of the NCTL for Formal Education: Yvonne Spicer
Vice President of Publishing: Rich Blumenthal

National Center for Technological Literacy (NCTL)
*Engineering Education for All*


The goal of the NCTL is to foster appreciation and understanding of the human-made world
by infusing technology and engineering into K–12 schools and museums nationwide. By
applying science and mathematics as well as engineering processes, children and adults will
solve real world problems and learn about the creation and implications of technologies.
For more information, visit nctl.org.

# Field Test Teachers

**Original Draft Version**

**Massachusetts**

Spencer Bernstein, East Bridgewater

John Chiffer, Gloucester High School

Ramiro Gonzalez, Boston Arts Academy

Fred Hopps, Beverly High School

Kurt Lichetenwald, Gloucester High School

Rick Meurillo, Ipswich High School

Thomas Rosa, Milford High School

Nancy Schalch, Beverly High School

Marc Seiden, Boston Arts Academy

John Skorupski, Belchertown High School

**Second and Third Draft Versions**

**Maine**

Loren Arford, Mid-Coast School of Technology

Bill Thomas, Mid-Coast School of Technology

William Thompson, Piscataquis Community High School

**Massachusetts**

Charles Acquista, Monument Mountain Regional High School

Kurt Barkalow, Career Development Center School

Joy Bautista, Boston Arts Academy

Chris Beaton, Ashland High School

Spencer Bernstein, East Bridgewater High School

James Besarkarski, Lunenburg High School

Burton Bjorn, Sutton High School

John Blackington, Wareham High School

Kevin Blute, Mashpee High School

John Burns, Agawam High School

Sharon Campsey, Taconic High School

Leo Carey, Charlestown High School

Rachel Chagnon, Boston Community Leadership Academy

Lawrence Cheever, Canton High School

John Chiffer, Gloucester High School

Mike Clark, The Engineering School

Ken Cody, Newburyport High School

Pasquale Compagnone, South Shore Charter Public School

James Connolly, Holliston High School

Chris Connors, Duxbury High School

Ken Cray, Greater Egleston Community High School

Keith Davis, Drury High School

Jim Dellot, Dedham High School

Beth Dichter, Northampton High School

John Donohue, Worcester Vocational High School

Shaune Ducharme, Shepherd Hill Regional High School

Mary Durkin, Tyngsborough High School

Brenda Erickson, Murdock Middle High School

Nicole Finnie, Quaboag Regional Middle/High School

Ted Fiust, Arlington High School

Mike Fontaine, Murdock Middle High School

John Fusco, Winchester High School

Mark Gaddis, Northbridge High School

Franklin Garcia-Mansilla, West Roxbury High School

Mike Gargan, Danvers High School

Michelle Getherall, Woburn Memorial High School

Blake Gilson, Beverly High School

Ramiro Gonzalez, Boston Arts Academy

James Gorman, Northbridge High School

Tom Gralinski, Amherst-Pelham Regional High School

Mark Greene, East Longmeadow High School

Tom Gusek, Worcester Vocational High School

Dave Haluska, Dedham High School

Lisa Henderson, TechBoston Academy

Mark Herman, Norwell High School

Fred Hopps, Beverly High School

Norm Immerman, Drury High School

Gary Janulewicz, Mashpee High School

Charles Kacamburas, Winchester High School

Ross Kowalski, Norwell High School

Thomas Kress, Northampton High School

Kevin Lauritsen, Worcester Vocational High School

Todd Les, East Longmeadow High School

Kurt Lichtenwald, Gloucester High School

Michael Looney, Mashpee High School

James Louis, TechBoston Academy

Robert MacMillan, Shrewsbury High School

Teresa Marx, Excel High School

Rick Merullo, Ipswich High School

Karla Montano, Tyngsborough High School

Dan Moriarty, Whitman-Hanson Regional High School

Peter Nassiff, Burlington High School

Dan Nelson, Milford High School

Sal Nocella, Mashpee High School

Rich Nycz, Norwell High School

Mark O'Malley, Lunenburg High School

Matt Ostrander, Wahconah Regional High School

Victor Pereira, Excel High School

Ann Perry, Bishop Feehan High School

David Potts, Nauset Regional High School

Joseph Ramos, Somerset High School

Bruce Rawley, Millbury Memorial Junior-Senior High School

Bob Richard, Pembroke High School

Elizabeth Roberts, Monument Mountain Regional High School

Thomas Rosa, Milford High School

Don Ross, Dedham High School

Deborah Rossman, Pathfinder Regional Vocational Technical High School

Niki Russell, Frontier Regional School

Nancy Schalch, Beverly High School

Luke Simpson, Chatham High School

John Skorupski, Belchertown High School

Richard Skrocki, Shepherd Hill Regional High School

Stephen Smith, Newburyport High School

Helen Sullivan, Tyngsborough High School

Karen Tatro, Gateway Regional High School

Allyn Taylor, Burncoat High School

Joye Thaller, The Engineering School

Bill Travers, Danvers High School

David Utz, Wahconah Regional High School

Phil Vachon, Burlington High School

Ray Vallee, Murdock Middle High School

John Vdovjak, Ludlow High School

Laurette Viteritti, Swampscott High School

Dave Vose, Canton High School

Anja Wade, Quaboag Regional Middle/ High School

Erica Wilson, The Engineering School

David Young, Hopedale High School

### Michigan

Joe Grigas, Lake Fenton High School

Jennifer Tews, Lake Fenton High School

### New Hampshire

Scott Edwards, Woodsville High School

Karen Fabianski, Conval High School

Ken Martin, Laconia High School - Huot Technical Center

Gil Morris, Conval High School

### New Jersey

Anat Firnberg, Tenafly High School

John Grater, Burlington County Institute of Technology

Frances Kenny, North Arlington High School

James Lincoln, Marylawn of the Oranges Academy

Peter Murdoch, Marine Academy of Science and Technology

Michael Polashenski, Mountain Lakes High School

Kenneth White, Mountain Lakes High School

Dario Sforza, Secaucus High School

Curt Rodney Taylor, Delran High School

Dennis Villavicencio, Plainfield High School

Geraldv Votta, Williamstown High School

Robert Weldon, Burlington City High School

### New York

Rayhan Ahmed, Metropolitan Corporate Academy

Ayodeji Awolusi, Freedom Academy High School

Sharon Percival-Calder, Freedom Academy High School

### Pennsylvania

Josh Elliott, Carl Sandburg Middle School

Kevin Hardy, Gettysburg Area High School

### Vermont

Carl DeCesare, Southwest Vermont Career Development Center

Adrian Sebborn, Southwest Vermont Career Development Center

# Acknowledgements

The Project Team at the Museum of Science, Boston would like to thank the original group of teachers and their students who field-tested the early drafts, as well as the teachers and students who tested the second and third drafts of the curriculum. The quality of the materials is largely due to their critical comments and wonderful ideas for improving the projects and text.

We also want to express our heartfelt thanks to these individuals who contributed significant time and creative ideas to bring the essential qualities of engineering to all high school students: Louise Allain, Grafton; Stephen Bannasch, Concord Consortium; Michael Baron; Jeff Bindon; Richard Boohan; David Bouvier, Framingham High School; Diane Brancazio, Belmont High School; John Burns, Agawam High School; Peter Cheng; Per Christiansen; Joseph Clement, Beverly High School; Jeff Coda; Charley Corley, Winchester Middle School; Marilyn Decker, Boston Public Schools; Angel Dos Santos, Tech Boston; Pat Dube, Beverly High School; Robert Damus; Ari Epstein; Hans Fuchs; Tom Gilbert, Northeastern University; Brian Gravel, Tufts University; Steve Gundrum, Pinkerton Academy; Chris Harper, Pinkerton Academy; Slater Harrison; Friedrich Herrmann; Mark Holthouse, Westwood High School; Fred Hopps, Beverly High School; Eduard Job; Georg Job; Ted Kahn, Design Worlds for Learning; Ken Klayman, Wachusett Regional School District; Eric Klopfer; Allen Kubicki, Dougherty High School; Sarah Low, Pinkerton Academy; Pat Maroni; Beth Miaoulis; Robert Moeser; Juan Paniagua, Northeastern University; David Perron, Pinkerton Academy; Beth Powers; John Scalese, Pinkerton Academy; Kristin Sharpe, Pinkerton Academy; Christine Shaw; David Shipstone; Steven Smith, Newburyport High School; Katy Snider, Pinkerton Academy; Mel Steinberg; Howard Stone; and Haruna Tada, Tufts University.

Special thanks are due to the teachers and their students who invited us to film the videos that accompany the Teacher Guide: Nancy Schalch, Fred Hopps, and Joe Clement, Beverly High School; Dan Moriarty, Whitman-Hanson Regional High School; Chris Connors, Duxbury High School; and Joy Bautista, Boston Arts Academy.

We also thank our colleagues at the Museum of Science for their collaborative spirit and hard work: David Murray, Lydia Beall, Becki Hosier, Nancy Levoy, John Pickle, Henry Robinson, Lesley Kennedy, Jeff Mehigan, Isabel Lopes, Christian Irwin, Michael Habib, Bohnn Barrayuga, Shirley Theodore, Jane Ko, Ben Simms, and Richard Phannenstill.

This program was made possible through grants from the U.S. Small Business Administration, Massachusetts Technology Collaborative Renewable Energy Trust, Lockheed Martin, Cisco Systems, Inc., National Institute of Standards and Technology, and the Highland Street Foundation.

# Introduction

You already have plenty of experience with technology, even if you have never taken a course about it. Just look out your window. Human-made objects—roads, cars, benches, homes, telephone wires, playgrounds—most likely fill your view. Look around the room. Can you find any objects that weren't designed by people? Now, consider all of the different technologies that you have used today, starting from the moment you got out of bed: your toothbrush, your shower, your clothing, the cereal box that holds your breakfast, and even the cereal itself. You might have a hard time thinking of a moment in your daily life when you aren't using technology in some way. No doubt about it: You are an active participant in the designed world.

This world didn't happen by accident. The technologies in it were purposefully created by engineers to meet human needs and wants. But even if you have no plans to become an engineer, your choices as a citizen and a consumer will influence what technologies are developed and how. In order to understand how your daily decisions create the world that future generations will inherit, you must become technologically literate.

What does that mean? Technological literacy means knowing how to use new technologies. It means understanding how new technologies are developed. And it means having the skills to analyze how new technologies affect us, our families, our work, our nation, and the world. Technological literacy is a tool for thinking about some of the most complex questions of our time.

- *What can we do to help our nation and others overcome serious health and environmental problems?*

- *What's the best way to develop cities and towns so that the people who live in them are happier, healthier, and more prosperous?*

- *How can our nation become less dependent on pollution-producing energy sources, and what's at stake if we don't?*

There are no straightforward answers to these questions. But as technologically literate individuals, we can chart the best courses of action for ourselves and our communities.

This course is built around questions. Through projects and activities, you will figure out for yourself how things work and why. As you build your technological literacy skills, you'll also develop increasingly complex answers to these questions:

**What is technology?**

Technology refers to everything that people do to change the world to meet human needs and wants. Technologies aren't just objects like computers, telephones, or satellites, but complex systems like those found in factories, waste treatment facilities, schools, and even homes. Through this course, you'll become more aware of the vast range of ways in which you interact with technologies every day.

**What do engineers do?**

Engineers design running shoes, computer chips, cell phones, swing sets, skyscrapers, and any other technology you can think of. Regardless of what they design, all engineers use some form of the design process—a way of thinking about problems that leads to creative and effective solutions. In this course, you'll play the role of an engineer, using the design process to develop your own technologies. You'll also learn about the lives and work of real engineers by reading the first-person stories in this book.

**What does an engineer need to know?**

A structural engineer must understand matter and energy and be able to make the calculations necessary to ensure that a building can withstand an earthquake. An electrical engineer must understand electricity to develop a means of communicating with a spacecraft orbiting Saturn. All engineers use science and math. During this course, you will apply the science and math you learn to a variety of design challenges. You will also get an insider's view of some interesting careers.

**How do new technologies impact society?**

Technologies can have a profound effect on human societies—sometimes positive, sometimes negative. What would the world be like without purified drinking water, the automobile, or the Internet? Throughout this course, you'll analyze the effects of past and present technological revolutions. Perhaps, most importantly, you'll consider ways that your own actions will impact the world of the future.

Learning about technology will help you to participate more fully as a member of your community and a citizen of the world. Becoming technologically literate is an exciting and challenging journey that will profoundly change your perception of how the world operates and how you fit into the big picture. As you embark on this journey, we encourage you to reflect on how every new idea relates to your own experience. After all, the personal and professional choices you make throughout your life will ultimately shape the world. Indeed, you will engineer the future.

# Table of Contents

# UNIT 3. GOING WITH THE FLOW

# UNIT 4. POWER TO COMMUNICATE

# Book Overview

*Engineering the Future* tells the stories of real engineers, engineering students, technicians, and people who work closely with engineers. All of the chapters are based on personal stories, but of course they are not complete—it is impossible to compress a lifetime into just a few pages. Each chapter communicates not only what people do on a day-to-day basis, but also what prompted them to choose this career, and the motivation that keeps them excited about their work. Finally, each chapter presents important concepts about engineering, science, and mathematics in the context of real-world engineering jobs. The book is divided into four units, each containing seven to nine chapters. On the following pages is a brief overview of the units, and the people you will meet in each one.

## Unit I   Manufacturing and Design

Our world is filled with technologies—objects and systems designed by humans to fulfill human wants and needs. How did this come to be so? In this unit, you'll explore this question by meeting nine working engineers and learning about how they design, build, and mass-produce the technologies that make up the designed world.

**Amy Smith,** an engineering instructor at the Massachusetts Institute of Technology, explores the concepts of engineering, science, and technology and explains how she designs tools that improve lives half a world away.

Inventor **Shawn Frayne** shares the design process—an approach to solving engineering problems—and explains why it's more of a guideline than a rule.

**Araceli Ortiz,** a former manufacturing engineer at Ford Motor Company, tells the story of the automobile's rise to fame and explores how companies decide what to mass-produce.

**Jamy Drouillard,** an aeronautical engineering student with high-tech dreams, describes his own design process.

**Dudley Green,** a process engineer at Teradyne Corporation, shows that every product and every technology is a part of an interconnected system that is, itself, designed.

**Lam Loc,** a Computer-Aided Design (CAD) technician, explores engineering drawing techniques and explains why a picture is worth more than a thousand words to engineers.

**Christine Epplett,** a developer at New Balance Athletic Shoe, takes us through the process of designing and mass-producing popular footwear.

**Robert Hartmann,** an electrical engineer at an industrial design firm, explores how companies use the design process to develop products for market and examines why a product's look and feel is as important as how it functions.

Inventor **Saul Griffith** illustrates why nature knows best when it comes to building better manufacturing systems.

## Unit 2　Sustainable Cities

A city is an ever-changing, designed system filled with structures of all sorts, like houses, apartment buildings, factories, and stores, as well as subsystems, such as those that control traffic, water, electricity, and waste. A city's various structures and subsystems must evolve constantly to meet the changing needs of its residents. In this unit, you'll learn how designers draw on their knowledge of mathematics and science to design structures and systems that will stand the test of time, promote the health and well-being of residents, and preserve more of the natural world.

**Peter Park,** an urban planner in Denver, describes the key elements of the world's greatest cities as well as a new-and-improved design for his own.

Field engineer **Kirk Elwell** explores the various forces and loads that a structure must be designed to withstand as he describes the design and construction of a major Boston bridge.

"Green" architect **Chris Benedict** tells why conventional heating systems can be bad for the environment and how to design a building that conserves energy while keeping its inhabitants warm.

Structural engineer **Bill Baker** explains how he's engineering the worlds tallest structure to withstand sky-high forces.

Geotechnical engineer **Cathy Bazán-Arias** explains why engineers need to understand the land they are building on.

**Prity Rungta,** a construction manager in Toronto, Canada, describes the complexity of building a house on time and on budget.

**Lauren Stencel,** a college student, describes how she's helping to build a home that uses the sun for its energy needs.

Our world is filled with technologies—objects and systems designed by humans to fulfill human wants and needs. How did this come to be so? In this unit, you'll explore this question by meeting nine working engineers and learning about how they design, build, and mass-produce the technologies that make up the designed world.

**Bob Brown,** design engineer at Woods Hole Oceanographic Institute, describes how he's overhauling the deepest human-driven diving submersible in the country.

Astronautical engineer **Aprille Ericsson** shares how she's designing a spacecraft that will bring Martian material back to Earth.

Professor of thermodynamics **Ron DiPippo** describes how geothermal wells might provide a solution to some of the problems associated with burning fossil fuels for energy.

Activist **Josh Tickell** tells the story of how he reworked his diesel van to run on leftover cooking fuel.

**Rebecca Steinman,** a nuclear engineer, explains how a nuclear reactor is designed to provide electric power safely without creating air pollution.

**Chris Langenfeld,** design engineer at DEKA Research, explains why it's sometimes better to look to history when designing a low-emissions wheelchair.

Environmental engineer **Lisa Bina** leads a tour of a major city's sewage system and explains how it has been redesigned to protect residents.

## Unit 4   Power to Communicate

Every time you turn on a light, you are depending on a vast electrical system known as "the grid" to supply electricity to the bulb. In this unit, you'll find out how electricity is generated and distributed to millions of people daily. You'll also explore how electrical systems are integral to communication technology such as telephones, the Internet, cell phones, and satellite systems.

Computer scientist **David Clark** describes the digital world of computers and explains his role in designing the Internet to inspire innovation.

**Sol Lerner,** a computer programmer at ScanSoft Corporation, explores the complexity of developing systems that can "understand" human speech.

Chemical engineer at the National Energy Technology Laboratory **Soung-Sik Kim** explores how electricity is generated and how her designs are making the process more efficient.

**Nanette Halliburton,** a test engineer at Cisco Systems, Inc., explains how information can travel encoded as light though fiber-optic cables and traces an e-mail message from sender to receiver.

Electrician **Ken McAuliffe** explains how the Museum of Science, Boston is wired to ensure that the building's systems get the electrical power they need.

Carnegie Mellon communications engineer **Alex Hills** examines how he developed satellite communication systems in rural Alaska and how that work allowed him to pioneer wireless networking technologies.

**Christine Bordonaro,** a materials engineer at Evergreen Solar, introduces the concept of renewable energy and describes how engineers have harnessed the energy of the sun to generate electricity.

Museum of Science curriculum developer **Joel Rosenberg** shares a model for electricity that he found while designing this course with the hope that he can help students overcome some of the barriers he faced trying to understand electricity.

Entrepreneur **Jim Gordon** describes how his current venture, developing a wind farm off the coast of Cape Cod, highlights the benefits of renewable energies and illustrates the controversy that surrounds energy technologies.

# Manufacturing and Design

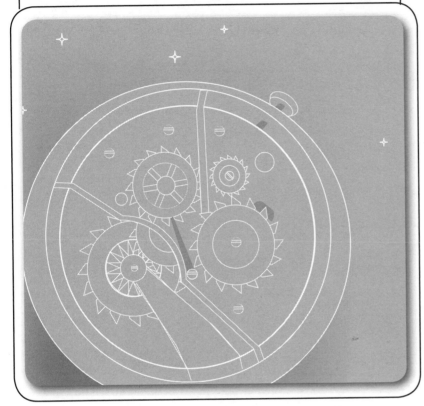

# 1

# *Welcome to the Designed World*

## Amy Smith

Many people think that the term ***technology*** refers only to computers, cell phones, and other electronics. But technology refers to anything people do to change the natural world to better suit human needs and wants, even something as simple as preparing and cooking the food we eat. With this definition in mind, think about all the different ways humans have changed the natural world to gather and prepare food. Consider all the technologies involved in growing and harvesting crops, and delivering them from the farm to the market. All tools and equipment we use to prepare our food, such as refrigerators, cutlery, pots, stoves, ovens, and so on are technologies, too! We even need technology to dispose of our food wastes in the town landfill. Just about the only thing that doesn't involve any technology is the process of eating.

Map of Haiti

I'm Amy Smith. I teach at the Massachusetts Institute of Technology (MIT), a university in Cambridge, Massachusetts. I specialize in creating technologies for people to use in the developing world.

Besides teaching soon-to-be engineers, I also have a laboratory at MIT where I work with my students to create new technologies for people living in rural villages in Haiti and other developing countries. Why does Haiti need new methods of cooking? Well, while most people in the United States use gas- or electric-powered stoves, many people in Haiti only use charcoal as a cooking fuel. Charcoal is made from wood; meeting the demand for wood has led to widespread *deforestation*. Ninety-eight percent of the forests in Haiti have been harvested, resulting in wildlife habitat loss and soil erosion.

Still, Haitian villagers have many good reasons for using wood charcoal as a cooking fuel. It's cheaper than other fuels, and it's very easy to find. Widespread unemployment has led to poverty in many communities in rural Haiti; many people simply cannot afford any other fuel. Some people even have difficulty paying for charcoal.

In the next chapter, one of my students will tell you more about how we are developing a new cooking fuel that may help combat environmental degradation and poverty in rural Haiti. But first, I want to tell you why I became a mechanical engineer.

I'll start by explaining what engineers do. ***Engineers*** improve existing technologies or create new ones to meet human needs or wants. The English words "engineer" and "ingenuity" originate from the same Latin root, *ingeniare*, which means to devise or invent. ***Technicians*** are people who operate, repair, and maintain equipment; as such, they participate in engineering projects, too.

There are many kinds of engineers. You may already know that electrical engineers invent and improve cell phones, computers, and hearing aids, or that civil engineers design bridges, skyscrapers, and low-cost housing.

**Engineers**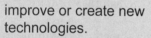
improve or create new technologies.

**Technology**
refers to everything that people do to change the world to suit human needs and wants.

**Scientists**
investigate the natural world and how it functions.

Do you know that, among other things, environmental engineers find ways to reduce the impact of our technologies on the environment by designing sewage systems, or that chemical engineers develop chemical ways to purify drinking water? Mechanical engineers, like me, are best known for creating new machines, but in reality, our work tends to overlap into other branches of engineering. My projects are good examples of how different engineering fields interact.

Another common misconception about engineers is that we are scientists. *Scientists* observe and investigate how the natural world functions, develop explanations for why things happen, then conduct experiments to see if their explanations are right. *Engineers* use the laws and theories that scientists develop to design new technologies. Engineers and scientists actually have a reciprocal relationship. Scientists often use new technologies to aid them in their pursuit of knowledge. A microscope is an obvious example of a technology that helps scientists study the natural world. You can imagine there is some overlap such that a chemical engineer must know a lot about chemistry to design a chemical process that purifies water. Likewise, a civil engineer must have a good understanding of physics if she wants her bridge to bear the weight of a locomotive.

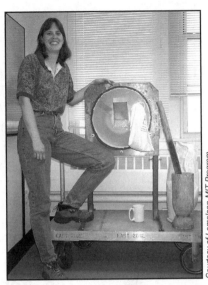

Amy Smith was the 2000 winner of the $30,000 Lemelson-MIT Student Prize.

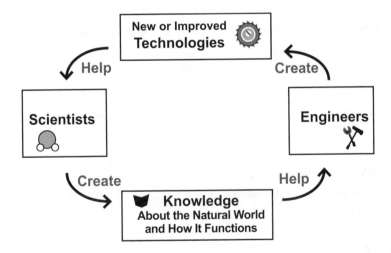

Technologies come in all shapes and sizes. Scientists who study animal behavior have claimed that humans are not the only ones who shape their surroundings to suit their needs. Most birds build nests. Beavers construct dams. Scientists have even observed chimpanzees using twigs as tools to extract termites from tunnels. But humans are, by far, the greatest users and inventors of technology. In fact, people who study the past have named major periods of human history by the prevailing type of technology, from the Stone Age to the Information Age.

## The Stone Age   2 million years ago
started with the development of stone tools. In the Stone Age, people developed ways to harness fire for heating, cooking, and protection.

## The Bronze Age   6,500 years ago
began with the discovery of copper and other metals. Agricultural technologies increased the reliability of food supplies and the growth of cities.

## The Iron Age   2,500 years ago
was defined by the use of iron and steel for tools and weapons. During this period, people migrated from farms to towns and cities for work.

## The Middle Ages   500 A.D.–1400 A.D.
saw the development of technologies, including book printing, the water wheel, and mechanisms for creating paper money.

## The Renaissance   1400 A.D.–1750 A.D.
was a period of rapid advances in technology. The name Renaissance, which means "re-birth," described the revival in art, science, and architecture.

## The Industrial Revolution   1750 A.D.–1900 A.D.
saw the invention of machinery to run factories and power vehicles. During this period, workers flocked to cities for factory jobs.

## The Information Age   mid-1900–present
gave birth to computers, the Internet, and tremendous advances in science and technology.

In your opinion, what will the next age be called?

# Technologies That Cross Borders

My interest in engineering first expressed itself around the dinner table when I was growing up. During family meals, I'd talk with my parents about how a motor worked or how to prove a math equation. My father was an electrical engineer and my mother a math teacher, so conversations like this were pretty common in our house. Their attitude about solving problems—mathematical and otherwise—led me to study engineering at MIT. After graduation, I entered the Peace Corps, a government organization that sends Americans all over the world to help people.

The Peace Corps sent me to the African nation of Botswana as a math and science teacher. One afternoon, as I was looking out over the Kalahari Desert from my kitchen window, I realized that, as an engineer, I might be able to develop new technologies that could help people in Botswana and countries like it. I decided to go back to school to get more training as an engineer so I could learn how to make a difference for people in *developing nations,* nations where the standard of living and average income are much lower than in the United States, Canada, and Japan.

As a graduate student at MIT, my first field experience gave me an opportunity to create a technology for people in rural Senegal. In many Senegalese communities, women make flour by grinding grain by hand. It's backbreaking work. I once spent about three hours grinding enough grain to make a cup-and-a-half of flour! Using a motorized technology called a hammermill, a person can grind enough grain in one minute to make twelve or thirteen cups of flour. However, a hammermill requires a metal screen that separates the flour from the hulls of grain. When the screen breaks—and they all eventually do—the hammermill is useless. Most communities that use hammermills cannot afford to replace the screens and don't have the equipment to make new ones. Hammermills with broken screens gather dust, while women return to pounding grain by hand.

Women in rural Senegal grinding grain by hand. It is backbreaking work.

My screenless hammermill

After studying the hammermill dilemma for a few months, I figured out a way to use the air that flows through the mill instead of a screen, to separate the particles of wheat. This technology increases the lifespan of the hammermill by many years. The screenless hammermill I developed uses less fuel than the original hammermill and costs about a quarter of the price.

The screenless hammermill is an excellent example of an **appropriate technology**—a technology that can be manufactured, maintained, repaired, and improved with local community resources. The screenless hammermill seldom breaks, and if one does break, it's easily repaired with commonly available materials and tools.

In the courses I teach at MIT, students learn how to invent appropriate technologies that can be used for microenterprise. A **microenterprise** is a small business that can be run by an individual or a family. A family might use a screenless hammermill to make and sell their own flour, or they might charge others a small fee for using the mill. Some of these new businesses have been very successful at helping people rise above the poverty line. If the technology also reduces human impact on the environment, that's an added benefit.

## Patents

After devising a new technology, many engineers apply for a patent. A **patent** is a document the government issues granting an inventor the sole right to make, distribute, or sell a particular invention for a specified number of years. Most engineers patent their designs. If a company wants to manufacture and sell an invention, the company must get written permission from the inventor. It's illegal to make or sell an invention without that permission. The patent system ensures that engineers get appropriate credit and compensation for their work.

Obtaining a patent for an invention can take a long time. The inventor must submit detailed documentation with evidence proving that he or she invented the device in question. The paperwork even includes signed copies of the engineer's notebook! The U.S. government keeps extensive records of patents, dating back hundreds of years. When developing new technologies, engineers often conduct patent research by studying old patents to learn how other engineers developed related technologies.

> A **patent** is a document issued by the government that gives an inventor the sole right to make, distribute, or sell a particular invention for a certain number of years.
>
>

I chose not to patent the screenless hammermill I developed because I wanted people around the world to be able to make, distribute, and use the technology without having to get my permission and without having to pay a fee. That's an unusual decision; most engineers are quick to patent their work.

## Technologies Are Everywhere

Technology is such an important part of being human that, like breathing, we hardly notice it. Pause for a moment and take a close look at this book. What technologies were involved in creating it? How many different technologies can you see from where you are sitting right now? I don't mean just cell phones and computers, but also pencils, papers, chairs, and many more.

Some of these technologies are used all over the world, but many technologies don't cross borders very well. Engineers like me must always consider available resources when designing products for users in other countries. Take, for example, an incubator. An incubator is a device that can keep its contents warm for a long time. Doctors in American hospitals routinely use incubators for several purposes, such as caring for babies born prematurely or culturing bacteria to diagnose disease. Incubators run on electricity. While many communities in rural areas of developing countries would benefit from having incubators, these areas often lack access to electricity. Clearly, it wouldn't make sense to ship a bunch of incubators to these communities. Incubators wouldn't be an appropriate technology in those places. It makes much more sense to redesign a technology or create a new one that suits users' particular needs. So I invented an incubator that works with inexpensive chemicals that maintain the same temperature for a long time after they are heated without using any electricity. This incubator is ideal for the developing communities I'm interested in helping.

As an engineer, I find developing appropriate technologies to be very satisfying work. It's a special kind of challenge to create a new technology for people in other parts of the world—and, of course, I get to travel a lot. But everyone who enters the field of engineering or technical trades has different motivations for doing the work that he or she does. You'll learn more about that by reading this book.

##  What's the Story?

1. How has engineering been important in human history? Give at least three examples.

2. What is the difference between a scientist and an engineer?

3. According to Amy's definition, the term "technology" refers to anything you do to change the world to suit human wants and needs. List at least ten different technologies you have seen or used in the past hour. List five technologies that may have been involved in the production of this textbook.

4. What does the term "appropriate technology" mean? Give an example of an appropriate technology. Give an example of a technology that is not appropriate.

5. What is a patent, and what motivates engineers to patent a new technology they develop?

## What Do You Think?

6. How can teamwork lead to better solutions? Why is it valuable to have people with different backgrounds work on a team? Give an example from your own experience.

7. Imagine that you've been hired as a consultant by the International Red Cross to help determine the best ways to foster economic growth in a country where most of the people are very poor. One member of your team is interested in finding American companies to set up branch offices to provide well-paid work for locals. Another team member says it's better to help the people establish their own microenterprise. What course of action do you think is better and why? Be sure to define the term "microenterprise" in your answer.

8. Describe a personal experience you've had in solving a design problem.

# Birth of a New Technology

## Shawn Frayne

Courtesy of Shane Frayne

**Key Concepts**
**from Previous Chapters**

1 Engineering

1 Technology

1 Microenterprise

Now that Amy has told you what engineers do, I'm going to tell you how they do it.

My name is Shawn Frayne, and I work as a research assistant in Amy's laboratory. To be honest, I never really liked school all that much when I was growing up in Tampa, Florida. It never felt like I was learning how to do anything revolutionary. I didn't feel challenged to think in new ways. I took Amy's class on microenterprises during my last year in college, and I finally realized I could use my engineering training to solve problems in important and new ways.

I'm thrilled to still work with Amy even though I've graduated. I joined her class while I was still in school, but, unfortunately, I was a little too late. I had just missed their trip to Haiti!

I've heard that it was an incredibly cool trip. Amy and her students traveled to Maissade, a small town about an hour and a half north of Port-au-Prince, Haiti's capital. The town is rural, and most of the people who live there are farmers.

Amy told you about the problems caused by using charcoal as a cooking fuel. I want to tell you how our team used the engineering design process to invent a new cooking technology. People use the engineering design process as a guide to invent just about everything, from paper clips to rocket ships.

When I tell the story of how we developed the technology, it may not sound as if we followed any kind of process at all, but we did. I'll tell the story first, and then I'll describe the steps we took in the design process. Amy's team knew that wood charcoal was contributing to significant problems in Haiti. The team wanted to create a new fuel, one that didn't rely on wood. Although wood was available, it was not plentiful and we wanted to avoid the need to cut down more trees. This new fuel could not make a lot of smoke when burned, because most people cook indoors and smoke fumes can be toxic, especially to children.

The group arrived with a plan to shred scrap paper and press the shreds into pellets that could be burned. Sounds like a great idea, doesn't it? The team used a heavy press to make the pellets. They spent the first several days in Haiti redesigning the press, so the process would take less time. When the team tried to light a pellet with a match, however, it didn't burn very well at all.

It wasn't until the group returned to MIT—around the same time I joined the project—that we burned the pellets and discovered they didn't burn hot enough to even heat water! We thought about trying to improve the paper pellets, but reconsidered this approach because the scrap paper solution had other drawbacks. The village where the team worked produced very little scrap paper, so the team traveled all the way to Port-au-Prince to get it. Burning pellets just did not fit our plan to develop an appropriate technology, which had to use easy-to-find local materials. We were disappointed, but not discouraged or surprised. That's engineering! Failure is essential to the process. Every failed attempt offers new information that helps in the next try.

We decided to search for other flammable waste products that are easily available in the village. The travelers noticed plenty of sawdust in Maissade. We tried to make pellets from sawdust, but the pellets just crumbled. We needed something to make the sawdust stick together, something we could find in the village. A student from Ghana suggested using a sticky oatmeal-like substance, called cassava flour, that people eat in his country. Cassava is a root vegetable much like a potato, which also grows in Haiti. Haitians make it into a pancake-like dish.

We found some cassava flour, cooked it, mixed it with the sawdust, and then pressed the mixture into pellets using our press. When it dried, the pellets held together. Was this the solution? Not quite. When we lit the cassava-sawdust pellet, it produced even more smoke than wood charcoal did! Another failure, but we had new information to help us get closer to a solution.

Again we searched for plentiful and cheap materials. The team recalled that near the village they'd seen piles and piles of crushed sugar cane, which is left over after the sugar-making process. A lot of sugar cane is grown in Haiti. People there turn the canes into sugar by pressing the juice out of them, then boiling the juice down. After juicing the cane, Haitians often dry some of it to use as fuel for the boiler. Because of this process, we thought the dried sugar cane stalk might make a good fuel. However, we also knew it produced a lot of smoke. Outside, where most Haitians make sugar, the smoke is not a problem. For indoor cooking, we needed a fuel that made very little smoke.

Still, we decided that dried sugar cane stalks, called bagasse, just might work. To solve the smoke problem, we burned the bagasse in a container with very little air. This process burns off a lot of the smoke, so all that remains are lumps of powdery black carbon.

We formed briquettes by cooking cassava paste, mixing the paste with the black carbon powder, and shaping the mixture by hand. The hand-shaped briquettes dried as hard pellets. When we tested them, the charcoal sugar cane pellets burned hot with very little smoke. Finally, we had developed a solution made from locally available materials that burned well and didn't make much smoke. Success at last!

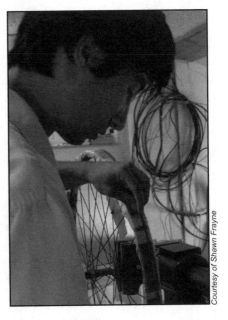

It had taken months of experimenting to find a solution. We felt satisfied we had found something that might work. However, we weren't quite finished. We still needed to test the sugar cane briquettes in the lab to see if the fumes they produce were truly less toxic than wood fumes. We also had to find a faster way to produce the pellets than shaping them by hand. We wanted to make it possible for one or two people to produce enough charcoal briquettes to sell and earn a decent living. Finally, if we overcame these obstacles, we'd need to help some of the Haitian *entrepreneurs*—creative people willing to try new business opportunities—get access to the raw materials and equipment needed to make the charcoal briquettes. No easy task! I've learned that the technology is an important part of the process, but making the business that gets people that technology is sometimes a greater challenge.

## The Engineering Design Process

Our process of developing this technology didn't follow a straight line, but we did follow the steps of the engineering design process. Here are the steps:

### 1. Define the problem.

The design process always starts with defining the problem. Before developing a new technology, engineers must try to understand the problem in detail. With this understanding, engineers can decide what features and requirements are necessary for the technology to solve the problem. The requirements include both the criteria or desired features and the constraints or limitations in developing or using the technology. Constraints often include costs, time, and materials.

---

- **Problem:**
  People in Haiti cut down trees to make fuel, which leads to environmental degradation.

- **Criteria:**
  Provide an environmentally friendly, easy-to-produce alternative to wood charcoal. Provide Haitians the opportunity to develop microenterprises around the technology.

- **Constraints:**
  The solution cannot cost very much to produce and cannot give off toxic smoke when burned. This new technology cannot be made from wood. The fuel must be made of locally available materials.

*Engineering the Future: Science, Technology, and the Design Process*

## 2. Research the problem.

There are many ways to research a problem. Library and Internet research showed us that wood-based fuels contribute to serious ecological problems in Haiti and elsewhere in the world. We did patent research to learn about other people's ideas for solving similar problems, which helped us decide to use a press to make scrap paper into pellets.

When my classmates arrived in Haiti, they did a lot of research on locally available flammable materials by looking around and asking questions. Researching a problem simply means learning all you can about it.

## 3. Develop possible solutions.

The most creative part of engineering is developing many different ideas for solving a problem. Because individuals often think of unique creative solutions, our team used brainstorming to come up with as many ideas as possible. The team thought of many different ways to improve cooking technologies in Haiti, many of which we didn't even try. Regardless, each idea helped us to better focus on a plan that would work.

## 4. Choose the best solution.

No one can tell for sure what will be the best solution, or which technology will work best. But, at some point, an engineer must choose a solution that meets all requirements and test it.

## 5. Create a prototype.

Before engineers commit to a particular solution, they usually develop a prototype. A *prototype* is a full-scale working model that tests whether the technology meets the requirements. Prototypes rarely work as expected, but an engineering failure can be a benefit. Our first prototype, the shredded paper pellet, didn't burn well. We learned that we had to use a fuel that burned hotter and more easily. Our second prototype, the sawdust pellet, smoked too much. But the experience with these failures led us to the cassava flour and the invention of the sugarcane charcoal briquettes.

 ### 6. Test and evaluate the solution.

To truly crack a problem, the solution must meet all criteria and constraints. Cassava is easily available in Haiti, and the briquettes are easy to produce. We also eliminated the need to use wood, and we tested the briquette's flammability—it burned hot and produced very little smoke.

But our team's new cassava briquettes must meet all the other requirements as well. We still need to analyze the fumes in a chemistry lab here at MIT to ensure they are safe to use. If the fumes pass the test, we will need to determine whether entrepreneurs in Haiti can develop microenterprises to profitably produce and sell the briquettes.

 ### 7. Communicate the solution.

Another step in the design process is communicating the solution to the people who might use the new technology. We need to work with entrepreneurs in Haiti to describe the benefits of sugarcane charcoal briquettes and discuss how producing them may provide a source of income. This step might be the most important one because an unused technology is no better than an unavailable technology.

Informing entrepreneurs around the world about our charcoal briquette technology is part of my job right now. Amy and I have created a manual that explains how to make the briquettes. We've been distributing it to people Amy knows around the world from her time in the Peace Corps. Some people in the Philippines already have shown an interest in using the technology. I also created a website about this project and others like it. We often return to Haiti to work with entrepreneurs and engineers there to develop the briquette technology further. If our briquettes catch on, we'll help preserve the remaining trees in Haiti—and maybe help some entrepreneurs in Haiti start their own small charcoal-making businesses.

 ### 8. Redesign.

As soon as people start using a new technology, they usually find a way to improve it. Making improvements leads to changing how we define the problem, and the engineering design process begins again. If shaping each briquette by hand is too slow, then we need to add the requirement "briquettes must be made quickly" to our original design process. The team will have to research different methods for making briquettes and brainstorm ideas to speed up the production process. After we select the best idea, we'll have to build a prototype and start the other necessary steps in the process over again.

The engineering design process is a cycle. Every time we decide to improve an existing technology, the engineering design process gives us a map to find the solution.

### All Steps

Keep a notebook. Working engineers find it helpful to write each step of the engineering design process in notebooks. The purpose of the notebook is to keep all ideas in a single place, whether documenting an observation or testing methods and results. The engineer or the team can retrace each step in the process by consulting this one source.

Is it always necessary to follow each and every step of the engineering design process as if it were a recipe? No! Our team's failure with the paper pellet made us go back to the first step and continue our research. At each step in the process, an engineer must decide either to go back or move forward toward a successful solution.

For a long time, I had always wanted to take on this type of project—one where we would work as partners with people from around the globe, to invent something that makes a difference—but until I started working with Amy, I wasn't sure it was really possible. Fortunately, as part of her class at MIT, Amy has shown many students like me how the greatest technologies of the 21st century will show up on a small farm in Haiti, not just in the local mall. I'm lucky to be a part of some of those technological breakthroughs, starting with the sugarcane charcoal briquettes.

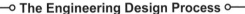

## The Engineering Design Process

**Define the Problem**
Describe criteria and constraints.

**Research the Problem**
Learn all that you can about the problem.

**Develop Possible Solutions**
Brainstorm creative solutions.

**Choose the Best Solution**
Choose a solution that best meets your requirements.

**Create a Prototype**
Make a working model.

**Test and Evaluate**
Test the solution and evaluate its success.

**Communicate**
Explain your solution.

**Redesign**
Suggest improvements to your solution.

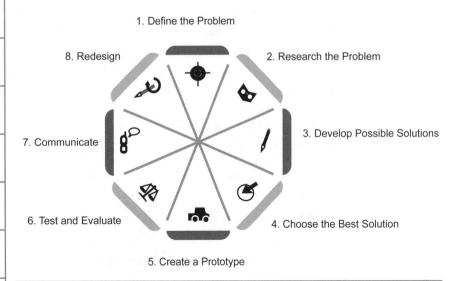

1. Define the Problem
2. Research the Problem
3. Develop Possible Solutions
4. Choose the Best Solution
5. Create a Prototype
6. Test and Evaluate
7. Communicate
8. Redesign

**Criteria**: the desired elements of the final product

**Constraints**: limitations to the design or the design process

## What's the Story?

1. What is the engineering design process?

2. Did Shawn's team follow the steps of the design process in order?

3. What's the difference between criteria and constraints?

4. How many prototypes did the team build? How many were successful?

5. Think about Shawn's response to his first failure. Was he surprised? What do engineers think about failure? How is this different from the way most people think about failure?

6. Why is communicating the solution an important step? What happens to technologies that are not communicated?

## Connecting the Dots

7. Amy Smith says that engineers use science to develop new technologies. At which point in the design process did the team use science in developing their new technology?

8. Why was it critical to use materials that were cheap and easy to find for a new cooking technology in Haiti?

## What Do You Think?

9. Your principal just hired you to help solve a problem for your school. Students are sneaking off campus for lunch because they are so unhappy with the food choices at the school cafeteria. The principal has budgeted only $1,000 to solve the problem, and she really wants it solved this academic year.

   How would you use the engineering design process to develop a solution to this problem? Write two or three sentences for each step detailing how you would accomplish it.

   Step 1: Define the problem, criteria, and constraints.
   Step 2: Explain how you would conduct your research.
   Step 3: Brainstorm at least three possible solutions.
   Step 4: Describe how you would choose the best solution.
   Step 5: Indicate how you would create a prototype.
   Step 6: Show how you would test your solution.
   Step 7: Explain how you would communicate your solution.
   Step 8: Describe how you might improve or redesign your solution.

## Aeronautical Engineering

**3**

# *Designs That Take Flight*

Jamy Drouillard

**Key Concepts**
**from Previous Chapters**

2 Engineering Design Process

2 Criteria

2 Constraints

2 Prototype

I'm an aeronautical engineer, which basically means that I design technologies that can fly. I know the charcoal briquette project did not involve any flying technologies, but like any engineering project, it did involve the design process, which is something I've had plenty of practice using.

My name is Jamy Drouillard, and I come from Haiti, which helped a lot during the trip to Maissade. Every day our team needed to communicate with the native people, especially when looking for new materials. Having spent the first 12 years of my life in Haiti, I speak Haitian Creole. But even beyond that, I understand people in Haiti. They trusted me to communicate what they wanted to say to the other students. Of course, I had never learned to talk about engineering in Creole, so I had some challenges translating what the students wanted to say. In the end, we learned how to ask the right questions.

You may wonder how I ended up at MIT. While I was growing up in Port-au-Prince, my parents taught me that education is important. Time and time again, they had witnessed how those who received a good education had better chances at creating prosperity for themselves and their families. By the time I was twelve years old, Haiti was in the midst of major political upheaval. Our president, Jean-Bertrande Aristide, had been forced into exile during a violent military overthrow of the government. The future felt uncertain for Haiti, and I remember that school was often canceled due to widespread violence. As a kid, I'd celebrated the extra days off. When I look back now, I realize that those were days I could have been in school learning.

My parents longed to find a more stable situation for me to get my education. My sister lived in Philadelphia, so I came to the United States to live with her. My mother moved here so she could work and support me. But my dad stayed in Haiti with the rest of the family, and he traveled back and forth often. I did well in school, but it wasn't easy, especially at first.

I attribute most of my success in school to my early interest in engineering. Back in Port-au-Prince, I loved watching *Buck Rogers* or *Lost in Space,* two popular sci-fi TV shows. I was also good with my hands. I could fix clocks or get our cable connection working. In Philadelphia, I went to a school that focused on science and math. I liked school, but I really enjoyed an after-school program called "SPARC!" That program showed me that creativity and fun are a big part of engineering. On some days, we'd pretend we were on a mission to Mars, and we'd build a mission-control room with lights and computers. We'd make space suits and act as if we were NASA engineers and astronauts. We even created our own astronaut-training program.

I didn't realize that what seemed like fun and games back then would lead me down my career path, but that's when I decided I wanted to build flying machines. I looked into several engineering schools. There are hundreds of schools and each has something unique to offer. I decided that MIT was the best fit because I liked what I'd heard about the aeronautics program. I spent four years getting my undergraduate degree in aeronautical engineering at MIT. I got to work with teams to design and build different kinds of airplanes and rockets. The experience was not unlike those early SPARC! days. In college, of course, we were trying to make real machines that actually worked. But the fun and excitement were still there for me—even more so.

Courtesy of NASA Glenn Research Center (NASA-GRC)

Now, as a graduate student at MIT, I'm trying to solve a different problem: building a small helicopter as a class project. It's nothing like the fuel problem I worked on in Haiti, but it does use the design process. I'll take you through my process:

 **1. Define the problem.**

For any engineering project, you must be clear about what problem you're trying to solve. On television, broadcast news channels are always trying to find the newest, most cutting-edge camera angles at fast-moving basketball games so they can attract a larger share of the television-viewing audience. We determined that a flying machine carrying a camera might be a great solution to this problem. The technology would have to be capable of flying around a court, controlled by radio, and sometimes navigated by itself. The flying camera would need to be able to follow a fast break while remaining a safe distance from the players and the audience. The machine should also take the camera up to the stadium ceiling for a bird's-eye view of the action on the court. The technology would also be designed to dispense coupons to spectators during halftime. The technology must not be too big or too heavy. If a heavy machine were to crash, a spectator or a player could be injured.

---

- **Problem:**
  Sports news channels want a new way to capture basketball games on camera so they can attract more viewers. (While most people use the word "problem" to describe something bad or troubling, engineers often use the term to describe a need or desire that a new technology is designed to satisfy.)

- **Criteria:**
  The technology must be able to carry a small camera, track a player, make maneuvering decisions on its own, and be radio-controlled. It must also be able to dispense coupons. Its design must minimize the risk of injury or damage if it falls or malfunctions. It must be able to fly for seven minutes at a stretch and carry about a quarter-pound of weight.

- **Constraints:**
  The device can't be larger than 1.5 feet long and 1 foot tall or weigh much more than 6.5 pounds.

---

## 🐱 2. Research the problem.

There are many ways to research this problem. We watched some videotapes of basketball games to determine how players move around a basketball court. We went to several basketball stadiums to take measurements of the court, the stands, and the space between the court and the stadium ceiling. We even talked with stadium managers and news camera operators to learn more about what other technologies are currently used to record games.

Next we looked at how other people have solved similar problems. Sometimes small blimps are used to distribute coupons to audience members, but they move too slowly to keep pace with a fast break. And there are quite a few small and maneuverable remote-controlled helicopters already on the market, though none of them are used to hold cameras at sports events. We decided to build one of these helicopters to see how well it met our requirements.

We built a small, remotely operated helicopter from a kit. Building the helicopter was a great way for me to learn more about the science principles behind how helicopters operate. It's essential for an engineer to understand the science concepts relevant to his or her design projects. Otherwise, the engineer would have to rely exclusively on trial and error to develop an improved design. By understanding the science, an engineer can make a good prediction about whether a particular design will operate the way he or she intends.

The model helicopter works just like a full-size helicopter. It is lifted off the ground by the main rotor, which has four blades, each of which is like a small airplane wing. The helicopter's engine spins the rotor, pushing air downward, which lifts the helicopter. This upward lift can be explained by a fundamental physics concept: For every action, there is an equal and opposite reaction. It's not unlike when you do a push-up on the floor: When you push down on the floor, your body is lifted in the opposite direction with the same force. In this case, the rotor pushes air toward the ground and is lifted toward the sky. Asa soon as the helicopter leaves the ground, however, the machine's body tends to spin in the opposite direction as the rotor for the same reason. To prevent that from happening, a smaller rotor is mounted on a boom—a long arm that extends from the body. This rotor pushes air in the opposite direction of the spin, which counteracts the body's tendency to spin.

Jamy creating a cardboard model.

After building the first model, we discovered that the design had some serious drawbacks: It was too heavy, and in the event of a malfunction, the large rotor could injure someone. In addition, this helicopter was very hard to control. This helicopter clearly did not meet our requirements, but because helicopters are easily maneuverable, move quickly, and can carry weight, we decided that some type of helicopter still might work.

*Photo taken by Cary Sneider*

We looked at other small helicopters on the market. My professor found some toy helicopters that had three or four main rotors rather than just one. Helicopters with three or four main rotors work a little differently from conventional helicopters. Each of the small rotors on the top provides lift. The tilt of the rotors has an effect much like a boom, giving the helicopter stability. The rotors are small, making it less likely that someone would be injured if the helicopter fell, a big advantage from our team's standpoint. And these helicopters seemed to be much more stable. However, none of them were powerful enough to carry a small camera. Most of them could just lift their own weight.

Toy helicopter with three main rotors

 **3. Develop possible solutions.**

After some thorough research, our team felt convinced that a helicopter design would work. We developed a handful of possible solutions. Most of the designs were helicopters, larger than the toy helicopter but smaller than the model helicopter, with three or more small rotors instead of one large one. Each design used a different material. One design had a durable plastic for the body of the helicopter, for instance, while another used a lightweight aluminum frame.

 **4. Choose the best solution.**

To compare and choose the best possible design, I created a computer simulation of how these helicopters might fly. I could simulate how the helicopter would handle in tight turns or chase a player to the other side of the court. In this way, I "experimented" with different designs before spending the time and money to build a prototype.

I also created some simple cardboard models. Building these simple models really helped me see how the different designs might work. Of course, engineers can never be sure they've selected the "right" design—there's always a design that might be better. At some point, an engineer must make an "educated guess" and choose one solution.

 **5. Create a prototype.**

My team is still in the process of selecting a "best" solution. Then we'll actually build our design to see if the idea will work. As Shawn commented, the first prototype rarely works as expected, but they are an excellent method of showing where a design fails. As an essential part of the design process, prototypes let you discover design problems early on.

**6. Test and evaluate the solution.**

Our team will have to build and test several prototypes before we get one that will work. For those early tests, we'll probably tie different weights to the prototype to see how much weight it can carry. Then, we'll test it somewhere it can't hurt anyone if it fails—maybe in a big, empty gym. If it doesn't pass the test, we'll have to go back and work on the prototype some more or try an earlier idea. With the engineering design process, you can always go back to an earlier step.

 **7. Communicate the solution.**

After we think we have found a good design that meets our criteria and constraints, we'll need to communicate the solution. When I was an undergraduate, I would usually make a class presentation to communicate my solution to the teacher and the other students. However, if we get this design working well, we may want to patent it and maybe even present the idea to a company that would manufacture and sell it.

Communicating the idea to others in a clear and persuasive way is just as important as every other part of the engineering design process. If people don't understand your idea or don't think it's important, they won't use it.

**8. Redesign.**

It's a safe bet that whatever we develop will need improvement. As people begin to use the technology, they'll encounter flaws in the design, parts that break, or new features they'd like it to have. Of course, before we make any changes, we'll need to be clear about what needs to be changed and why, which means we'll start defining the problem again. Because the engineering design process is cyclical, you can always return to an earlier step. I think you shouldn't jump steps, but not all engineers share this opinion.

During the engineering design process, an aeronautical engineer—in fact, any engineer—needs to consider all of the negative consequences of a new design. You wouldn't want to create problems that are worse than those you're trying to solve. That's one reason our team must be so careful about making sure our helicopter cannot possibly hurt an audience member or a player—even if it malfunctions and flies directly at someone! We also have concerns that the helicopter might distract players or get in their way. We're trying to predict any negative consequences so that we can lessen the chance of their happening. It can be frustrating to toss out months of work because a promising solution turns out to have an unanticipated negative consequence.

*Engineering the Future: Science, Technology, and the Design Process*

**Keep a Notebook.**

As with every engineering design process, we keep accurate notes and ensure that we record this information in our project notebook.

## Future Projects

When I look into the future, I don't see myself fooling around with toy helicopters forever. My dream is to work on space vehicles. I want something that I designed to hover over a Martian landscape. But, as we learn from the design process, we have to take one step at a time, right?

○—— **Jamy's Comments on the Engineering Design Process** ——○

| | | |
|---|---|---|
|  **Define the Problem** | Problem definitions must include requirements for the solution, such as criteria and constraints. | |
|  **Research the Problem** | Researching the problem often includes looking at how others have tried to solve the problem before. | |
|  **Develop Possible Solutions** | Getting creative new ideas isn't always easy. | |
|  **Choose the Best Solution** | I can never be sure I've selected the "right" design...but I have to stop fiddling at some point and choose what I think is the best solution. | |
|  **Create a Prototype** | The first prototype rarely works as expected, but it's a great way to see where it fails. | |
|  **Test and Evaluate** | If it doesn't meet the test, we'll have to go back and work on the prototype some more, or try one of the earlier ideas. | |
|  **Communicate** | Communicating the solution is as important as every other aspect of the design process. | |
|  **Redesign** | It's a safe bet that whatever we develop will need to be improved. | |

## 📖 What's the Story?

1. What problem is Jamy trying to solve?

2. How does Jamy research the problem?

3. Jamy was a member of the team that went to Haiti. What else did he contribute besides his engineering skills? How did his contributions help the team?

## ⊖ Connecting the Dots

4. How is designing a helicopter similar to designing a new cooking fuel for Haiti?

5. Like Shawn, Jamy talks about the importance of communicating the solution. But the two engineers must communicate their solution to very different audiences. Who is Shawn's audience? Who is Jamy's?

6. Jamy says that engineers should always follow the steps of the design process in order, even though the engineers can go back to earlier steps and start over if necessary. Would Shawn agree with that? Which engineer is right?

## ✴ What Do You Think?

7. Jamy thinks it's a safe bet that whatever his team develops will eventually need to be redesigned. Why do most technologies need to be redesigned?

8. Every engineer has different motivations. Jamy loves the creative aspects of engineering. To him, developing a new technology is fun, sort of like playing a game. Amy Smith and Shawn Frayne are motivated more by a desire to help improve the quality of people's lives. What might motivate you to learn about or develop new technologies?

# *Beyond Words*

## Lam Loc

**Key Concepts**
**from Previous Chapters**

**2** Engineering Design Process

**2** Communicating the Solution

Imagine using only words to describe your design for a bridge to your construction team. It's not easy! Sure, you may get across a general idea of the design, but how long would you have to talk? You'd probably be talking for a long, long time to convey all the necessary design details, such as the thickness of each steel beam, the angle of each cable, or the size of each nut or bolt. It's often said that a picture is worth a thousand words. In engineering, a picture may be worth hundreds of thousands of words—and a lot of time!

I should know. I spend my days creating drawings that help engineers communicate their ideas more effectively. My name is Lam Loc. I am a Computer-Aided Design (CAD) technician at HNTB, a firm based in Kansas City with offices all over the country.

The company designs transportation systems, bridges, airport systems, sports stadiums, and even plans for cities. These massive construction projects require hundreds and thousands of design details.

I always saw myself working in architecture or graphic arts. Growing up in Guangdong, a province next to Hong Kong, China, I loved looking at structures and trying to understand what kinds of decisions went into their design. I even started an art club in my high school. The club members would get together to study drawing, painting, or anything to do with art. I didn't know any architects or engineers while growing up and didn't really have a clear sense of how I might become an architect myself. But I knew that if I worked hard and applied myself, I'd find a way.

After high school, I came to the United States to live with my brother, who had moved here several years earlier. I felt that I'd have more opportunities to pursue my dreams in the United States than I would have in China. When I arrived in America, I knew very little English, so I worked in restaurants and took English as a Second Language (ESL) classes at night. Over time my English improved and I began looking for an opportunity to learn about design or architecture.

I found out about a year-long CAD program being offered at the school I attended. CAD, or Computer-Aided Design, refers to computer programs that allow engineers to create precise drawings of their design ideas. I realized that learning CAD might be a good way to start working in the field of engineering. Just about every engineering and design company needs CAD technicians, people who have specialized training in using CAD systems.

In my first class, I learned techniques for drawing by hand. Our instructor would bring an object to class—say, a birdhouse or a hair dryer—and we would create precise sketches of the object. To draw an object by hand, I had to examine it very closely. In a sense, I had to learn how to look at an object in a new way, by noticing how all of its surfaces and details were oriented in space. After learning the basic principles of hand-drawing, I began studying how to create drawings using computers.

After I earned my certificate, I was hired as a draftsman-in-training by a large engineering company in Boston. I trained for a year before becoming a draftsman. After working at the same company for the next couple years, I found my job at HNTB. I love my job, even though it can get stressful at times. I sometimes work late in the evenings or on weekends to finish my work on time, but I don't mind spending my extra time drawing. Even when I'm not working, I often spend my free time designing my own website or other working design projects.

## Drawing and the Design Process

Every company and probably every engineer approaches the design process a little bit differently. In large companies like HNTB, the design process is slightly different than the process described in earlier chapters. At HNTB, the design process begins when a prospective client needs to design a structure or some other system. The client may be a government agency that is planning to build a new section of highway, or perhaps a corporation that wants to construct a recreation facility for its employees. Typically, a client contacts several firms like HNTB and asks each firm to submit a proposal.

Our engineers and architects thoroughly research the client's design problem and then develop some possible solutions. They often make sketches of their possible solutions to share their design ideas with one another. Each company offers a proposal to the client, who chooses the proposal that best meets their design requirements.

That's where I come in. Instead of building a prototype, I create several three-dimensional (3-D) design drawings. These drawings are created to give the client a sense of what our design would look like and how it would function once constructed. Engineering firms used to make 3-D models of their proposed design, but building models is as expensive as it is time consuming. Using CAD software, we can create realistic drawings that illustrate a design with less cost. Design changes are less expensive, too! We simply edit the drawing on our CAD systems. We can get a revised proposal to a client quickly using CAD technology.

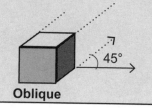

**Oblique**

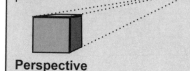

**Perspective**

## A Matter of Perspective

Humans have not always been able to represent 3-D objects very convincingly. In fact, before the Italian Renaissance, which started in the 1400s, artistic drawings were hardly realistic.

In an *oblique drawing,* the front side of the object appears flat in the picture plane and the sides and top of the object are at a 45-degree angle to the horizontal lines of the front side. These angled lines are half as long as the lines of the actual object, which creates a sense of depth. However, oblique drawings do not look very realistic.

In the early 15th century, the Italian architect and engineer Filippo Brunelleschi developed a mathematical theory for creating 3-D drawings that resulted in much more realistic depictions. Brunelleschi studied the way people viewed objects in space. A number of artists had experimented with ways to improve representations of 3-D objects, but Brunelleschi was the first to find a scientific explanation for how humans see in 3-D.

He observed that when we look at an object, the object's parallel lines appear to converge on an imaginary point on the horizon. This imaginary point is called the *vanishing point.* To draw an object that looks realistic, the front face of the object can be drawn as a flat, two-dimensional (2-D) shape, but parallel lines moving away from the viewer must be drawn so they seem to converge at a vanishing point in the distance. All of Brunelleschi's original drawings and paintings have been lost, but his system, called *perspective drawing,* has been used and further developed by many other artists.

"Marriage at Cana" by Giotto (1267–1337). This painting was made prior to the use of perspective drawing.

*Courtesy of Wikipedia*

"Christ Handing the Keys to St. Peter" by Pietro Perugino (1446–1524). This painting uses perspective drawing.

*Courtesy of Wikipedia*

Using CAD software, I can create nice-looking 3-D images that have multiple vanishing points. Look at this perspective drawing of the top of a tower that HNTB designed for a bridge in Ohio last year. It actually has two vanishing points, which gives the impression that the viewer is looking at the object from one of its edges.

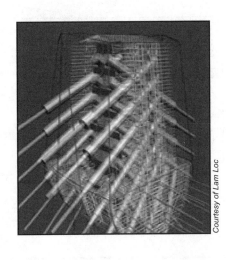

Now, perspective drawings are a wonderful way to showcase a design to a client because they look so exciting and dynamic. But for engineers, perspective drawings have some drawbacks—the big disadvantage is that it is impossible to know the dimensions of an object by measuring a perspective drawing. That's because the sides of an object are drawn the way the viewer sees them, not at their true lengths.

Look at the two images of a simple cube below. On the left you see an oblique drawing of a perfect cube with sides that are two feet long and two feet wide. (Remember: All sides of a cube are of equal length and width.)

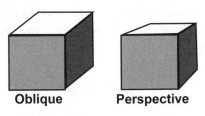

**Oblique**          **Perspective**

On the right you see a perspective drawing of the same cube. Do all the sides of the drawn cube appear to be the same length and width? If you used a ruler to measure the length of each side of the drawing, you'd find that they are not equal in length. In fact, if I hadn't told you that this shape was a cube, you could not have known that from looking at these two drawings.

This is why engineers depend on a different drawing method to convey information about the size and shape of an object. Engineers use an *isometric drawing* to represent a 3-D shape in two dimensions. All vertical lines are drawn vertically, but all horizontal lines are drawn at 30 degrees to the horizontal. The sides are not shortened as in an oblique or perspective drawing. As a result, isometric drawings of objects look a bit distorted to the viewer. Regardless of how they look, isometric drawings convey more meaningful information to the engineer than other 3-D drawings do.

In an ***isometric drawing,*** all vertical lines are drawn vertically, but all horizontal lines are drawn at 30° to the horizontal. Engineers can communicate the measurements of an object through an isometric drawing.

30°

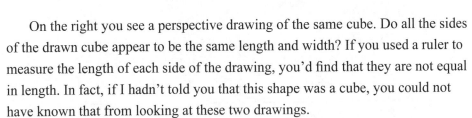

**Isometric**

## Scaling

A full-size drawing of a skyscraper or a bridge would be too big, so, I make my drawings much smaller than the true size of the object—sometimes as much as 10,000 times smaller. How do you convey the true measurements of an object when the representation is so much smaller than the object? I draw the object to scale.

*Scale* refers to the ratio of the size of an object in a drawing to the size of the object in real life. The *scale factor* is the ratio of the size of drawing and the size of the object. Suppose I want to make a scale drawing of a cube that is 82 inches on a side. If I draw the cube using a scale factor of one to ten (1:10), then each side would be 8.2 inches. If I use a scale factor of 1:20, then the each side of the drawn cube would be 4.1 inches.

To determine the length of any line I draw, I use the simple equation $x = sl$, where $x$ is the length of a line in my drawing, $s$ is the scale factor, and $l$ is the length of the real object. (In equations, $x$ is often used to represent an unknown number, while two factors written next to each other indicate multiplication.) For example:

$$x = sl$$

If $s = 1/10$

$$x = sl$$
$$= 1/10 \times 82 \text{ inches}$$
$$= 8.2 \text{ inches}$$

If $s = 1/20$

$$x = sl$$
$$= 1/20 \times 82 \text{ inches}$$
$$= 4.1 \text{ inches}$$

Original Size:
2 inches wide by
2 inches long

scale of 1/2
1 in. by 1 in.

## For Good Measure

Our company recently got a job building a bridge in India. Determining the dimensions for the drawings of that bridge will be a little more complex. That's because people in India use the **metric system** for measuring lengths. The metric system is a system of measurements in which the standard unit for length is one meter. Just about every country in the world except for the United States and Great Britain uses the metric system exclusively.

In the United States, we use the British system of inches, feet, and miles for measuring—but not always. As more and more American companies and organizations work in other countries, the metric system is becoming more widely used. In fact, many scientists in the United States now use the metric system for making measurements. Engineers still use the British system, but they do use the metric system occasionally. So they need to know how to convert between the British and metric systems. At the end of this book, you'll find a conversion chart that lists various metric units and their British equivalents.

| Metric System Prefixes | | |
| --- | --- | --- |
| Giga- | G | $10^9$ |
| Mega- | M | $10^6$ |
| kilo- | k | $10^3$ |
| hecto- | h | $10^2$ |
| deka- | da | 10 |
| deci- | d | $10^{-1}$ |
| centi- | c | $10^{-2}$ |
| milli- | m | $10^{-3}$ |
| micro- | μ | $10^{-6}$ |
| nano- | n | $10^{-9}$ |

*Engineering the Future: Science, Technology, and the Design Process*

As you can imagine, it would take a long time to calculate all of the dimensions of a complex object such as a bridge or a highway. Fortunately, the CAD software does most of these calculations for me. All I need to do is enter the design dimensions, choose the scale, and select the British or metric system. Of course, this saves a lot of time, and the calculations are very accurate. Still, I need to understand how to scale a drawing or convert from feet to meters. That way, if the CAD software generates an image that is not a correct representation of a design, I can figure out why and correct the problem.

## Back to Two Dimensions

While isometric drawings are very useful for communicating the dimensions of a design, they can only represent three sides of any object at a time. To view all sides of an object, draftsmen use orthographic drawings. An ***orthographic drawing*** is a two-dimensional (2-D), or flat, representation of a 3-D object using views of each side of the object. An orthographic drawing of a house is shown here.

To get a sense of how an orthographic drawing is created, imagine a house inside a glass box (1). Next, imagine standing directly in front of each side of the box and tracing the sides, top, and bottom of the house directly onto the glass (2). You now have a drawing of each view of the house drawn on the glass (3). Finally, imagine unfolding the glass box so that it lays flat (4) to give you an orthographic drawing of the entire house.

Of course, many orthographic drawings are much more complex than this one. To the bottom right is a front drawing of the same bridge in Ohio. As you can see, I put a lot of information into each drawing. In this view, I've labeled all of the dimensions of the structure. I can even use color coding to distinguish one material from another.

It's always satisfying when a construction crew successfully uses my drawings to build a structure. My drawings were the major source of information for building a tower head in Ohio. The drawings allowed the HNTB engineers to communicate easily with all the different construction contractors. Knowing that my contribution helps gives me a lot of satisfaction and makes all my hard work and late nights worth it!

> **Orthographic** drawings are 2-D, or flat, drawings of each side of an object. They are very useful to engineers for communicating the dimensions of a design.

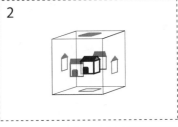

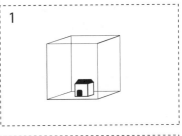

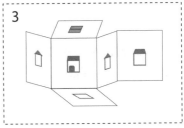

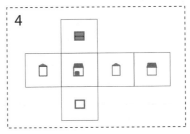

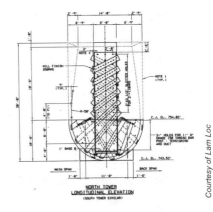

NORTH TOWER
LONGITUDINAL ELEVATION
(SOUTH TOWER SIMILAR)

 **What's the Story?**

1. According to Lam, what's the purpose of engineering drawing?

2. What do oblique and isometric drawings have in common?

3. Why was Brunelleschi's contribution to drawing important? (In your answer, describe his contribution.)

 **Designing with Math and Science**

4. On a piece of isometric graph paper, draw an isometric drawing of one of your books using a scale factor of 1:4. Be sure to list the book's measurements, and show all of the calculations you did to determine the measurements of the drawing.

5. Using quad-ruled graph paper, create an orthographic drawing of the same book using the same scale factor.

6. Use the conversion chart in the back of this book to determine how many centimeters long a football field is.

 **Connecting the Dots**

7. How does the design process at HNTB differ from the one that Shawn and Jamy used?

 **What Do You Think?**

8. Lam discusses how drawing helps his firm communicate design ideas to clients and construction teams. We all use drawings to communicate at some time or another. Describe a time when you used a drawing to communicate a message, an idea, or even an emotion.

---

**Types of Drawing**

**Oblique**

The front side of the object appears flat in the picture plane, and the sides and top of the object are at a 45° angle to the horizontal lines of the front side.

**Perspective**

A system for creating 3-D drawings that look realistic. In a perspective drawing, the lines of the object that move away from the viewer converge on an imaginary point called the vanishing point.

**Isometric**

All vertical lines are drawn vertically, but all horizontal lines are drawn at 30° to the horizontal. Engineers can communicate the measurements of an object through an isometric drawing.

**Orthographic**

2-D, or flat, drawings of each side of an object. They are very useful to engineers for communicating the dimensions of a design.

# 5

## *The Art of Engineering*

### Robert Hartmann

⚙ **Key Concepts**
**from Previous Chapters**

① Importance of Teamwork

① The Work of Engineers

Great art can have a powerful influence on your emotions. It might make you feel awestruck or reflective, it might fill you with rage or exuberance, or it might lead you to question something about yourself or the world. An artist's role in society is to create works that bring out an emotional response.

But art is not just something you find in a museum or a performance hall. There is a little art in every product that you use every day. The most successful products—and by successful I mean the ones that people are likely to buy and use—don't just work well, they also look and feel "just right." This brings up two important questions: Do engineers have to be artists to design technologies that appeal to people? And to what extent are artists engineers? After all, artists do alter the natural world to meet human desires.

There are no correct answers to these questions. Certainly, engineering and the arts both play an important role in the design of new technologies and products. That's something I have learned a lot about in recent years.

My name is Robert Hartmann, but most people call me Bob. I'm an electrical engineer at IDEO, a design firm based in California. While growing up, I was much more interested in numbers and sports than I was in, say, sculpture or photography. But when I look back, I've always loved to create things as much as any artist does.

When Texas Instruments came out with a programmable calculator in the 80s, I used it to invent a baseball game. And when I got my hands on my first personal computer, my friends and I programmed it to simulate motorcycle jumping and the motion of the planets. True, I might not have been making "art," but I was creating things to satisfy my own curiosity and others' as well—much like an artist would.

I had a difficult time deciding whether to study computer science or electrical engineering. I eventually decided to study electrical engineering at Union College in Schenectady, New York. I thought this field offered more chances for me to build things and seemed more hands-on than just using a computer.

When I graduated, I got a job working in Boston, at Polaroid's R&D Department—that's Research and Development—where I engineered new products. Polaroid is famous for developing instant cameras for the mass market. At one time hundreds of thousands of people in the United States and many European countries owned instant cameras. Polaroid also creates more expensive devices sold to niche markets. *Niche markets* are specialized markets that have fewer customers who are willing to pay more. When I was working at Polaroid, hospitals were one of our niche markets. I developed a printer for medical imaging, such as ultrasound, that doctors can use to see if embryos are developing into healthy babies.

***Mass market*** refers to all consumers in general.

***Niche market*** describes a specific group of target consumers.

I didn't realize it at the time, but during the design process, I always had to keep the look and feel of a product in mind. One time, I was experimenting with creating tiny circuits to run the automatic focusing and electronic timers on our instant cameras. Making these minuscule circuits was a challenge. The electronics had to fit into a very small space. Why? Most people want a camera that fits into their pocket or purse and looks sporty and refined, not one that's clunky and cumbersome.

## Making Objects with Attitude

A few years ago, a friend of mine who also worked at Polaroid told me about a job opening at IDEO. IDEO is famous for *innovation,* which means coming up with new products based on technologies that already exist. At IDEO I would have the chance to work on all kinds of innovations, from redesigning toothbrushes to improving entire railroad cars. I applied for the job and got it.

Working at IDEO, I really started to understand that a product's look and feel is as important to consumers as how well it works. Good designers understand how humans will interact with a product and that we have an emotional reaction to any object, whether it's a cell phone, a car, shoes, or art. We buy products that we feel match our personalities. Look at a cell phone. The newest ones look sleek and fit comfortably in your hand. The designers who created the phone understood that the size, shape, and color of the phone all express something that we, as consumers, can relate to. Some products have attitude, others give off a more conservative air. Still others strike us as practical or romantic. I find it amazing that we think objects can say so much about who we are. But we do. It's our nature.

In one case, a company came to IDEO with a new testing instrument they had invented. Workers used this machine to make sure parts were the right size and shape. While it worked really well, the company wanted us to improve its look and feel. Now, you might be tempted to think that people who buy factory equipment wouldn't care about a machine's look and feel, but they do! You can see in the pictures to the right the difference in the machine before and after IDEO redesigned it.

***Innovation*** involves making improvements to existing technologies, products, or methods of doing something.

***Invention***  is the process of creating new technologies that never existed before.

Courtesy of Medtronics

Courtesy of Medtronics

A testing instrument before (top) and after (bottom) IDEO redesigned it. Which one looks more appealing to you?

So, how can you design products that function well and have the "right" look and feel? One thing is certain: you can't do it alone. In fact, you need a whole team of people with different backgrounds who can bring their individual expertise to the task. At IDEO our teams are made up of different kinds of engineers, industrial designers, experts in design research, and specialists in user behavior.

The engineer's role is to understand enough about the natural world and science to make a design function well. **Industrial designers** focus on how an object looks and feels. **Human factors specialists** use the science of **ergonomics**—the study of how people interact with machines and systems in designed environments—to improve product design. They watch how products are really used and interview users and operators to understand their needs.

The team we assembled to redesign the test equipment closely followed this arrangement. Our team included these people:

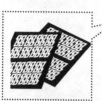  **Electrical engineers** redesigned the electronics and reduced its size to fit into the newly designed case.

  **Software engineers** reprogrammed the computer so that the graphical display on the screen would be easy to see and use.

  **Mechanical engineers** figured out how to manufacture the various parts.

  **Industrial designers** created the size, shape, color, and texture of the case.

  **Human factors specialists** observed how the instrument was used, then determined where the buttons should be and how large to make the display.

All of our work here is done in teams. In fact, we consider teamwork so valuable at IDEO that everyone who works in our office interviews applicants. I probably had interviews with thirty people before I was finally hired. Now I understand why. At IDEO you aren't hired just to do a job; you're expected to become a member of a team. Of course, teamwork can be difficult, because team members don't always agree. But we work together to resolve disagreements so we can define the problem and generate various solutions. Each team member can contribute ideas at every stage, and everyone knows how his or her particular expertise fits into the whole.

Our company is well known for redesigning a toothbrush for children. You might think that a child's toothbrush should have a small handle to fit a tiny hand. However, human factors specialists watched children brushing their teeth and noticed that children could get a better grip with a larger toothbrush handle. So the specialists consulted the industrial designers who figured out the shape and color of the product. Engineers on the team ensured that the materials held up under repeated use. The result was a brightly colored toothbrush with a large, soft, easy-grip handle. Another example of teamwork!

## Everything by Design

Recently, the company that operates the Acela Express high-speed train that runs between Boston and Washington, D.C., asked several firms to submit a bid to design the interior of the train. A *bid* is a price a company offers to a client for the work that needs to be done. I imagine that other firms submitted designs and estimated the costs for seats, windows, aisles, and such. But IDEO submitted a bid to design not only the interior of the train, but also the entire rider experience. We wanted to sculpt every step riders take, from the time they purchase tickets to the moment they depart the train at their destination. This approach required designing the entire rider experience, including the traffic flow at the ticket counter, the taste of the food, the feel of the seats, and all the other elements a rider sees and feels. I like to think we won the contract because we had a unique way of defining the problem.

Design is all around us. Just look at the doors and windows in the room where you are right now. Someone designed those. All man-made items are the result of someone's design. Even the experience of a school day, from the first bell to the time you leave at the end of the day, was designed and probably could be improved. Imagine if every public space were designed to give you the best possible experience. What would a hospital look like? How could you improve movie theaters? There are countless opportunities to improve our lives through good design. We take the path to innovation by questioning things as they are and thinking about how they might be improved.

## What's the Story?

1. According to Bob, how are artists and engineers similar? How are they different?

2. What does the term "innovation" mean? Give three examples of products that are innovations.

3. Give three examples of products developed for niche markets and three examples of products developed for the mass market.

4. What methods do engineers and designers at IDEO use to ensure their designs will have the right "look and feel"?

5. Why is it critical to have a diverse group of people on a design team?

## Connecting the Dots

6. How do the engineers who are improving technologies that already exist use the design process differently from engineers who are developing entirely new technologies? What individual steps might be different?

7. Engineers apply math and science while developing new solutions. In redesigning a toothbrush handle, how might IDEO engineers have applied math and science?

## What Do You Think?

8. Give an example of a technology that you use every day and would like to change. How would you improve it? Would you market it to niche or mass markets?

9. Bob says that working on a team is not always easy. Have you ever had a difficult time working on a team? If so, what did you do, or what could you have done to correct the problem? If not, why do you think your teamwork experiences have been so successful?

# 6

## *Bringing Designed Ideas to the Market*

### Araceli Ortiz

*Courtesy of Araceli Ortiz*

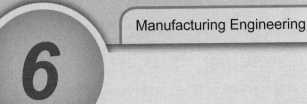

**Key Concepts**
**from Previous Chapters**

2 Researching the Problem

5 Types of Markets

The idea of manufacturing may seem totally removed from your daily life. But whether it's your shirt, your desk, or your locker, each one has been manufactured. Everyone's life is affected by manufacturing. Even if you're reading this under a tree in the middle of a forest, the book you're holding is manufactured.

Manufacturing technologies are systems of people and machines that change materials into useful products. In the process design cycle, engineers develop new technologies. Well, manufacturing turns those ideas and designs into products—media players, folding chairs, silverware, you name it.

My name is Araceli Ortiz, and I'm a manufacturing engineer. To understand why I became a manufacturing engineer, you have to know something about my family.

Courtesy of Araceli Ortiz

In 1994, I led a team charged with redesigning Ford cars to make them more appealing to women.

All four of my brothers and sisters are engineers. My siblings and I were inspired by our parents to improve other people's lives. After emigrating from Mexico City, my parents arrived in this country with little understanding of English or American culture—and without high-school diplomas.

But they had a strong work ethic and a solid vision of creating opportunity for their children. My father landed an assembly job at a Chrysler factory near our home. Everywhere I went as a child, I saw proof of my father's hard work—the cars driving around the streets of our town. His everyday work affected thousands and maybe millions of people.

That was my first encounter with the manufacturing world. Throughout grade school and high school, I studied science, engineering, and computer classes in the afternoon, after regular classes. I also learned what engineers do and decided to become one. After all, an engineering degree improves one's chances of finding well-paying work. I also liked knowing that I would be living up to my parents' dreams by making a successful life for myself and, eventually, for my own family.

## Designing a New Kind of Car for Women

As an engineer at Ford for 15 years, I got a chance to correct a big oversight in car design. In 1994, I became the director of women's product marketing. My job was to figure out how to redesign Ford cars to appeal to women. The company had done some research and found that, by and large, women were not buying Fords as often as they bought other car brands. Why not? Well, that's what I wanted to find out.

How do companies learn what consumers need? They conduct **market research,** the process of learning about consumers' thoughts and attitudes about products. Market researchers might conduct telephone or Internet polls. They might consult public records at the U.S. Census Bureau, which provides information on where people live, how much money they make, and how many children they have. The company might organize a "focus group," which is a panel of target users who talk about what they like or dislike about a certain product.

**Market research** is the process of learning more about consumers' attitudes and thoughts about products.

*Engineering the Future: Science, Technology, and the Design Process*

To conduct our market research, we invited women of all ages to join our focus groups. We asked the women why they chose to buy one type of car over another.

The women told us a lot about why they weren't buying Fords. Many of them couldn't reach the pedals without moving the seat closer to the steering wheel—not a safe place to be if the airbag inflates. Others couldn't see well over the dashboard or through the rear window. Some women said they couldn't reach the back door hatch when it was open.

After studying their feedback, we realized the problem: Our cars had been designed for men, and not just any man. Our cars were made to fit the average American male who is between 58 and 62 tall. Now, some women are this tall, but most—including myself—are not. Behind the wheel of a car, a woman my size could not clearly see the road and couldn't reach many controls.

It wasn't very difficult to find ways to redesign the cars to fit women better and be more attractive to them. We worked with a design team to install adjustable pedals that could be moved closer to the driver's seat; we lowered the windshield and rearview mirror; and we added longer strap handles to doors so anyone could easily pull them shut. Over the years, designers have added other ergonomic touches, such as a wide central console between the driver and passenger seats that can store handbags, and doors that close automatically after children are dropped off. I like to think that our work made our competitors design cars that are safer and more appealing to women, too. They had to if they wanted to keep up with us!

This example shows how social acceptance affects what gets mass-produced. To some degree, what people buy determines what is manufactured; buying a product helps ensure another will be made to replace it. When our earlier models were designed, few engineers considered women's needs. Most companies now realize that it's critical to consider all kinds of users as they design and produce products. For this reason, it's important to have as diverse a design team as possible. When companies don't design for a varied group of users, they may endanger the users they have overlooked. At the same time, they risk losing customers!

## The Car: A Case Study in Mass Production

People influence what kinds of products are manufactured by what products they purchase. But as soon as these products are widely used, they can take on lives of their own, affecting people and societies in profound ways. Cars are a fairly recent invention. In the late 1880s, just about everybody got around by bicycle, horse and buggy, trolley, train, or ship. By the turn of the 20th century, only a few companies made automobiles, by hand, and only the very rich could both afford them and have the time to learn how to drive them. Early cars cost between $3,000 and $6,000, a huge sum considering the average American's yearly income was only about $1,000.

Cars cost so much because it took so much time and labor to make them. In 1899, an automotive factory could build only about 100 cars a year. A skilled factory employee would build most or the entire car himself.

But then a young entrepreneur named Henry Ford, the founder of Ford Motor Company, had a revolutionary idea. He developed the ***assembly line system*** for manufacturing automobiles. In Ford's assembly line, the chassis, or frame, of the car was hooked onto a constantly moving conveyer belt. Workers stayed at stations along the assembly path and performed the same task repeatedly on multiple vehicles. As the chassis moved through the factory building, workers along the assembly line would attach the engine, the steering column, the fenders, and so on, until a complete car would roll off the conveyer belt. As soon as one worker finished a task, the next car would come along and the worker would start again.

The assembly line system boosted production of cars dramatically. The system allowed for ***continuous production,*** which means that products were built in a steady flow. In fact, after a few years of fine-tuning, Ford Motor Company could make cars six times faster than companies still building by hand. The assembly line is still widely used today.

Ford's Model T was first introduced in 1908.

Hey! Speed it up a little!

ETF CHOCOLATE ASSEMBLY LINE

The ***assembly line system*** allows for continuous manufacturing, whereby goods are produced at a steady rate.

*Engineering the Future: Science, Technology, and the Design Process*

## Economy of Scale

Because he could make so many cars, Ford sold his cars for much less money than his competitors could. He had achieved what economists call an ***economy of scale.*** An economy of scale is reached because, as production increases, the cost of producing each additional unit decreases. In other words, because Ford produced such a large number cars, each car cost less to produce.

To understand why, think of the price of a car as having four parts: 1) the cost of the materials; 2) the cost of labor to assemble the car; 3) the cost of the factory and machinery needed to produce the car; and 4) the profit made on each car.

**Materials**
cost less because it's possible to get discounts when buying large quantities of materials.

**Labor**
costs less if it's not necessary to train workers how to build an entire car.

**Factory and Machinery**
costs, sometimes called capital, are spread over the number of cars produced during the lifetime of the equipment.

**Total Profit**
is greater because more cars are sold.

To produce one car, a company would need to buy all of the materials, hire a team of skilled workers to assemble it, and a build a factory. To produce many cars, a company saves money by buying large quantities of materials. Labor costs are lower because the company can hire less-skilled workers to complete only one task, and these assembly line workers can produce more cars faster. Factory and machinery costs, sometimes called *capital costs,* are spread out over the number of cars produced during the lifetime of the equipment. Only one factory is needed whether the company makes 1,000 or 10,000 cars. The more cars a factory produces, the less each car costs to produce. Total profits grow as more cars are sold.

## How Did Ford Devise the Assembly Line?

Revolutionary as it was, Ford's assembly line didn't come out of nowhere. In fact, it was the result of manufacturing breakthroughs that started long before recorded history. Historians believe that the very earliest humans most likely made tools by hand for their personal use.

But today, manufacturing means not just making objects by hand but making them in a mechanical way for industry. Modern-day manufacturing began when early people started to specialize in making weaponry, clothing, and other goods. Instead of having to learn a little about a lot of different trades, people could dedicate themselves to mastering and improving processes and skills. Later, this approach produced a wide variety of goods and products.

Ford's assembly line system was an extension of this specialization, with each worker learning and repeating one task over and over on each car that came down the line. But assembly lines would never have been so successful without the contribution of another early inventor, Eli Whitney. Whitney best known for inventing the cotton gin, a machine that removes seeds from cotton, but he also built a firearms factory near New Haven, Connecticut, in the early 1800s.

*Engineering the Future: Science, Technology, and the Design Process*

Whitney realized that he could save time and money if his muskets were assembled from standardized, ***interchangeable parts.*** A trigger mechanism for one gun, for example, could fit into every gun in exactly the same way. A worker only had to learn enough about gunsmithing to install one size and type of trigger. Rather than hiring experienced gunsmiths, who were scarce and demanded high pay, Whitney could hire less-experienced workers and train them to do simple tasks.

Ford's assembly line depended on Whitney's idea of interchangeable parts, while another area of the factory used batch production. ***Batch production*** is the process of producing parts in quantity to be built into larger products. Steering wheels, tires, and windows were all produced in batches then attached to cars on the assembly line.

By the time Ford's assembly line caught on as a model for other factories, America's Industrial Age was in full swing. The British invention of the steam engine had boosted productivity and increased manufacturing jobs throughout the late 1800s. American cities grew as new workers, many of them immigrants, poured in to fill growing factories. The assembly line system pushed production even higher in the early 1900s, and that trend has continued until today. That's the reason I'm here. After all, my father immigrated here to work in the auto industry.

**Batch production**
is the process of producing standardized parts or components in quantity to be assembled later into larger products.

**Interchangeable parts**
are pre-fabricated standardized parts that are assembled into products. Before the advent of interchangeable parts, craftsmen had to make all parts by hand.

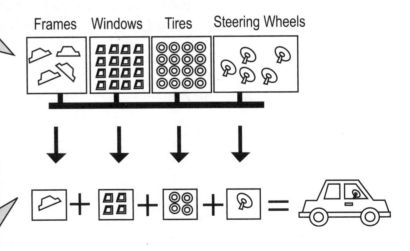

## Welcome to the Car Culture

With the assembly line system, Henry Ford could keep his prices low by producing a whole lot of cars. He charged less than $300 per car in the 1920s. Millions of Americans, not just the very wealthy, could afford them. By the late 1920s, over 26.5 million cars were registered in the United States, enough cars to seat every living American at the time. Cars became a symbol of mobility and freedom—the American way of life.

For these millions of cars, the federal government paved miles of roadway between cities and towns across the country. Voters insisted that politicians spend money to widen and improve city streets rather than improve public transportation systems. Suburban homes dotted the land outside cities, and the workers who lived in suburbia drove to and from work every day. Motels and fast food restaurants—the first ever—sprouted up along interstates, aiming to please road-weary motorists.

By the mid-1900s, the car had transformed America. The nation's highway system meant people could travel more easily, and the number of cars on the road grew. It became difficult for pedestrians to travel in most cities. Suburbs sprawled farther away from city centers. Cars had once been a luxury item, but now most Americans used them to get to work.

The car has had countless positive effects on American society, and they continue to improve the lives of Americans today. Our society is very mobile, thanks to our vehicles, which help us to get where we need to be—work, home, or at play. Ambulances bring patients to the hospital quickly. Trucks carry food, goods, and other necessities across the country. If cars and trucks could no longer be used, many parts of our society would come to a standstill.

But there is another side of the story. The rise of the car culture has led to a number of serious issues. Few could have anticipated how many car-related fatalities and injuries would result. The U.S. Department of Transportation reports that vehicles claim more than 42,000 Americans lives each year. Vehicles remain one of the leading causes of death in this country. Could the car's first designers ever have predicted that?

Our car culture has also affected the quality of our air. The Environmental Protection Agency (EPA) reports that, in many cities, the automobile is the single largest cause of air pollution.

These health and environmental costs represent unintended consequences of a technology. *Unintended consequences* are the unforeseen effects of new technologies that arise after a technology is accepted into everyday life—effects that the designers failed to foresee.

Not all unintended consequences are bad. The Internet's designers didn't predict that their innovation would lead to the World Wide Web giving millions of people instant access to information about almost any topic.

Just about every new mass-produced technology results in some unintended consequence. It's the responsibility of today's engineers to design products in a way that minimizes the possibility of negative consequences. Will engineers in the future avoid unintended consequences? Engineers can create diverse teams of experts to explore environmental, health, and other effects of emerging technologies during the design stage. But what can consumers do? Consumers can learn all they can about using a new technology before they buy it. Remember, even if you don't become an engineer, your decisions about technology will affect everyone's future.

> *Unintended consequences* of new technologies are effects that arise after technologies have become mainstream, effects that the designers failed to foresee.

## What's the Story?

1. What are manufacturing technologies?

2. List ten kinds of technologies that are manufactured.

3. Why had relatively few women purchased Ford cars before Araceli did her research?

4. How did Ford research the problem?

5. What is the difference between assembly line production and batch production?

6. Why are interchangeable parts critical for the success of an assembly line system? Be sure to define interchangeable parts in your answer.

7. Why is it more cost effective for companies to produce objects in mass quantities than it is for them to produce only a few?

## Connecting the Dots

8. Considering both the work at IDEO and at Ford, explain why market research is a valuable tool for companies.

9. How did Araceli use the engineering design process to change automobile design at Ford?

## What Do You Think?

10. Araceli asks two important questions at the end of the chapter: How can engineers avoid unintended consequences in the future? How much power do consumers have to minimize unintended consequences? Choose one question and answer it in a paragraph.

**7**

# *A Universe of Systems*

## Dudley Green

Photo taken by Rebecca Pierik

---

### ⚙ Key Concepts
**from Previous Chapters**

**4** CAD

**6** Manufacturing Technologies

---

The products of technology and engineering have powerful impacts on society—both good and bad. The story you just read about the mass production of the car would convince anyone of that fact. But remember that humans designed manufacturing technologies in the first place. That means we have the power to design products and manufacturing *systems* that minimize unintended consequences. Now, I'm not saying it's going to be easy! I'm just saying it can be done.

Before I go any further, let me tell you about my interest in systems. My name is Dudley Green, and I spend much of my time thinking about manufacturing systems as an engineer for Teradyne, a corporation with offices all of the world. I'm a process engineer, the engineer responsible for creating parts of manufacturing systems.

## What Is a System?

The manufacturing systems I work on build printed circuit boards. These circuit boards go into larger machines that test computer chips—the kind of chips you might find in a cell phone, a DVD player, a photocopy machine, a car, or a piece of medical equipment.

I've always been interested in systems—in how the parts of something work together to make something happen. When I was a kid growing up in Dorchester, a neighborhood in Boston, I was always in trouble with my parents for taking my toys apart. I wasn't trying to destroy the toys; I just wanted to see how they worked. My first bicycle, for instance, was a great mystery. But after taking apart the derailer, the chain, then the handlebars and the brakes, I gained a good idea of how my bicycle moved forward, stopped, and turned. The real problem, of course, was putting it back together again!

In high school I learned that taking toys apart was my early effort to figure out how my bicycle parts worked together as a system. Mathematics and science were my favorite classes in high school, but, well…let's just say that my grades did not always reflect my true love of learning. I was captain of the football team, and that focus often took up most of my time.

When I was accepted into Wentworth Institute of Technology in Boston to study mechanical engineering, I took apart all kinds of machines to see how their parts worked. Because I also needed to work full time to put myself through school, I got a job at Teradyne as an assembler on the factory floor. I assembled parts of circuit boards by hand. It was a good job, and it gave me hands-on experience to help me in the work I do now. All in all, it took me about ten years to get my diploma—but it was well worth the time!

Let me get back to telling you about systems because, to understand engineering, it's essential to understand systems. All circuit boards start as sheets of metal—gold, copper, or a combination of materials. Here's a picture of a gold circuit board that's nearly assembled. I'm holding my hand over a part of it because I don't want to give away any design secrets. Who knows? One of you may be working for the competition one day!

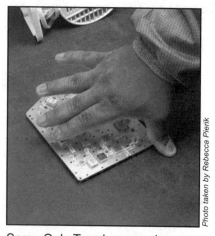

*Photo taken by Rebecca Pierik*

Sorry. Only Teradyne employees can see how our circuit boards are laid out.

*Engineering the Future: Science, Technology, and the Design Process*

A *system* is a group of parts that work together to achieve a specific goal. There are abundant examples of systems in the world; your own body is a living example. It's made up of systems of organs that work together to keep you alive. As Araceli told us, manufacturing technologies are systems that change materials into products. Manufacturing systems include the materials, machines, people, and resources used to mass-produce goods for the market. You'll learn about many other kinds of technological systems later.

Our factory uses an assembly line system. The circuit boards enter one end of the line and move along conveyor belts through machines and past workers. Like all systems, the assembly line can be broken down into inputs, processes, feedback, outputs, and goals.

*Inputs* include everything that enters the system to achieve the desired goal. To make a circuit board, you need natural resources, such as copper, gold, time, money, energy, labor, information, tools, training, machinery, and more. In a sense, you could even say that my education is an input to the circuit board manufacturing system at Teradyne.

*Processes* describe the parts of the system that actually change the inputs into the desired products. When you make cookies, your inputs are flour, sugar, baking powder, eggs, butter, and chocolate chips. But you must process these ingredients by mixing them, shaping the batter into cookies, and baking them in an oven. The mixing, shaping, and baking are your processes. No matter how great your ingredients are, if you don't have those processes, you don't have good cookies.

The manufacturing process at Teradyne includes a wide range of parts. In the first step of manufacturing a circuit board, a machine places a stencil over a blank board. The stencil, which I design, is a steel sheet with a cut-out pattern of all the electrical connections. The machine paints a paste made of tin and lead over the stencil. When the stencil is removed, the pattern from the stencil remains on the circuit board. Later, other machines attach the electronic components to this tin-lead paste pattern. All manufacturing processes use an orderly step-by-step procedure to complete an assembly.

*Feedback* provides information that the system uses to make adjustments during manufacturing. Feedback is critical during the process. Imagine if you put your hand on a hot stove and your nervous system failed to let you know your hand was burning. Your body, or any other system, needs feedback to operate properly.

A **system** refers to a collection of objects that work together to achieve a specific goal. All systems have:

- *inputs*
- *processes*
- *feedback*
- *outputs*
- *goals*

Photo taken by Rebecca Pierik

I designed this stencil to be used in the first part of the circuit board manufactuirng process.

Likewise, feedback can catch problems during the production process. In our process, the boards are extremely sensitive to temperature. Feedback helps us maintain the correct temperature, preventing cracking or other damage. Sensors detect temperature changes and send signals to the machine to raise or lower the temperature.

*Outputs* refer to everything the process produces. The desired output of our system is a fully loaded circuit board. Factory processes change materials into outputs that you might see in a grocery store or at the mall. Many manufactured items are *non-durable goods,* which means they are disposable. Disposable cameras, paper plates, or plastic utensils are designed to last only for a short time. Many electronics break or become obsolete quickly as well—even the circuit boards that Teradyne designs. *Durable goods,* on the other hand, stand the test of time. Cars, hand-tools, ovens, and furniture are all durable goods. Goods don't become durable or non-durable by accident. Engineers design goods to have a specific life expectancy. A disposable coffee cup is designed for one use, whereas a ceramic mug may last a lifetime.

There are other outputs to consider—and worry about. In the manufacturing of our circuit boards, flux fumes are an unpleasant output. Flux is a material that we use to clean our components. It has a foul smell and can irritate eyes and skin. If a machine gives off excessive fumes, a special sensor triggers an alarm. People respond like they would to a fire alarm, running for open air outside the building.

Many manufacturing processes produce pollution—noise pollution, air pollution, water pollution, and others—as an undesired output. While designing manufacturing systems, engineers consider these outputs and try to keep them to a minimum. Fortunately, flux fumes don't pollute our office air too often, and never without warning.

The *goal* of a system is whatever that system is meant to accomplish, whether it's producing the best chocolate chip cookies on the block or producing a million cell phones. The goal of our manufacturing system is to efficiently produce high-quality circuit boards. We're constantly trying to *optimize* the system, or redesign it in a way to make it run more smoothly and more economically. When our system falters, we waste valuable time and resources. What would happen if one of our sensors broke down and a machine scorched twenty gold circuit boards? Our company would lose a lot of money! Because we want to avoid waste, we continuously optimize our system to prevent such problems. After all, the more boards we make, the more we can sell.

> *Optimization*
> is the process of making a system as effective as possible. ★ ★ ★ ★

○ **Summary of a System** ○

|  | Definition |  | Example |
|---|---|---|---|
| **Inputs** | Everything that goes into the system in order to achieve the desired goal | $ | Copper or gold, time, money, energy, human labor, information, tools, training, machinery |
| **Processes** | The parts of the system that actually transform the inputs into the desired products |  | Stenciling, machining |
| **Outputs** | Everything produced by the processes |  | A fully loaded circuit board |
| **Feedback** | Provides information that the system then uses to make adjustments |  | If a temperature sensor makes a high reading, it will send a signal to a machine to start pumping in cool air |
| **Goal** | Whatever the system is trying to accomplish |  | Producing circuit boards efficiently |

**1**

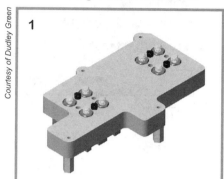

First, I used CAD software to design this piece of tooling, which will attach to a circuit board and protect parts of it from high temperatures.

**2**

Next, I used the CAD software to see how the components would perform. The lighter areas indicate where this shoulder screw, which fastens the whole piece on to the board, will experience the most stress.

**3**

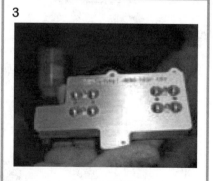

Finally, I sent my CAD file to the factory CAM system. That system used it to create this physical copy of my design.

# CAD/CAM: New Technologies Lead to New Systems

As you've probably noticed by now, a manufacturing system can be complex, requiring teams of people trained in different tasks, countless machines and controlling devices, and ongoing testing and improvement. Fortunately, some new technologies have emerged in recent years to make engineering manufacturing systems much easier to manage. For instance, I use Computer-Aided Design (CAD) software to create nearly all of my drawings.

CAD systems are a manufacturing engineer's best friend. Take, for instance, the "tooling" that I'm designing right now (figure 1). This piece of tooling will cover and protect the temperature-sensitive components on the circuit board as the board moves through a high-temperature chamber. I must be fairly confident it will work the very first time it's used; otherwise, expensive circuit boards may get destroyed.

With CAD, I can design the tooling to fit the board ahead of time. Then I can simulate how the tooling responds to different factors such as high temperatures or mechanical stress (figure 2). I can tweak the design to meet the process requirements before we build a prototype.

After completing the tooling, I simply send my CAD file directly to our factory's Computer-Aided Manufacturing (CAM) system. The CAM system uses the CAD file to control machines that produce the piece just the way I designed it (figure 3). CAM systems let manufacturers efficiently produce a wide range of goods from metal, plastic, and other materials. There are seldom any surprises, which is good for our golden circuit boards and our company profits.

# What's a System Again?

How can you pinpoint exactly where one system begins and another ends? It's very difficult to do that. In fact, when we try to define systems too narrowly, we may face trouble. Let me show you what I mean. CAD and CAM are systems that are embedded in larger manufacturing systems. Manufacturing systems are, in turn, a part of even larger production systems. What about the systems that provide inputs into the manufacturing systems? Or what about the systems that handle the outputs?

# Systems That Extract Raw Materials

Trees, iron ore, and oil are examples of raw materials—the natural, unrefined resources of the Earth. Some raw materials come from living things. Leather comes from animals, wood from trees, and cotton from plants. These are examples of renewable resources because they can be replaced in a relatively short time. Non-renewable resources, such as petroleum, coal, or metals, are not replenished after they're removed from a location.

Humans have created a variety of complex systems to find and gather raw materials. We've created systems that mine metals out of the Earth. Systems drill for petroleum and natural gas in deserts and in the ocean. We have systems to harvest plants and trees, and fish the seas.

# Systems That Make Raw Materials Usable for Manufacturing: Primary Processing

We don't pound gold into sheets at Teradyne. We buy the sheets from other factories located all over the country. Engineers develop systems that add value to raw materials by making them more useful. Systems that add value to natural resources range from cotton gins and fish processing plants to oil rigs and a wide variety of factories that smelt, mill, and refine raw materials.

These factories are responsible for what's called *primary processing*, the first step in transforming raw materials into useful materials. The plants that make gold boards start with either gold ore mined from the ground or recycled pieces of gold from electronics, old coins, and even dental work! Gold from all of these sources contains impurities that must be removed with heat and chemicals. After purifying the gold, the factory then melts it and pours it in a liquid form over large, flat brick molds. Finally, a machine rolls these bricks into sheets, which we buy and cut to the correct size and shape for our circuit boards.

Lumber mills process harvested trees into plywood, particleboard, and the two-by-fours used for construction projects of all kinds. Textile mills take truckloads of raw cotton, clean and dry it, spin it into thread, and then weave the thread into fabrics. Glass mills refine sand, then melt and shape it into sheets of glass.

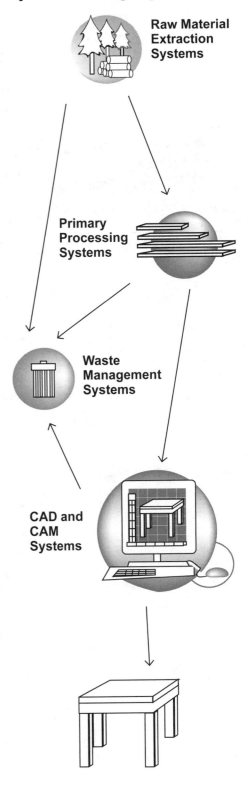

**Systems Working Together**

Raw Material Extraction Systems

Primary Processing Systems

Waste Management Systems

CAD and CAM Systems

## Systems That Deal with the Outputs: Waste Management

You might be tempted to think that the manufacturing system stops with the finished product, right? Well, I would argue that, given the number of non-durable goods in the marketplace, we must consider the systems that manage the waste resulting from mass production. What happens to the non-durable goods after we throw them away? Think about the complex system garbage collectors use to remove trash and then transport it to a recycling center, incinerator, or landfill. In 2005, U.S. residences and businesses produced more than 236 million tons of garbage, which is approximately 4.5 pounds of waste per person per day. American manufacturing facilities generate and dispose of approximately 7.6 billion tons of industrial solid wastes each year—more than thirty times as much!

> ***Primary processing*** is the first step in transforming raw materials into products.

## Putting It All Together: Life Cycle Analysis

All of the systems I've talked about so far are completely interdependent. Most systems depend on other systems. You'd have a hard time naming a system that functions independently from any other system. That's just how our world works. Fortunately, more and more engineers are designing their products with the big picture in mind.

In recent years, companies and government agencies have begun analyzing the total life cycle of products and services to gauge the true costs of different products by how they affect the environment. ***The life-cycle analysis*** of a product involves charting all of the inputs and outputs of every system related to its production and use—from extraction of raw materials to primary and secondary processing, use, and finally disposal. The sum of all of these inputs and outputs show what kinds of effects a mass-produced product has on our environment.

So, you can see that many systems are embedded in other systems, making them all interrelated. That's certainly true for natural systems, and it's true for man-made systems. Engineers and non-engineers must consider the impact of a product's life cycle on our environment. Asking ourselves "What is the whole system here?" will help us think outside the box. The more we remember how a system fits into the big picture, the more assurance we have that our technologies will truly help us live better lives.

##  What's the Story?

1. How does Dudley define the term "system"? What are the parts of a system?

2. Draw a diagram of a system for producing potato chips. Be sure to label the different parts of the system.

3. How do the goals of the potato chip production system differ from its outputs?

4. What raw materials would be necessary for this potato chip production system? What kinds of waste would the system generate?

5. What kinds of primary processing might be required for the potato chip production system?

6. List three durable goods and three non-durable goods that you use every day.

##  Connecting the Dots

7. What are the inputs, outputs, processes, feedback, and goals of an automobile manufacturing assembly line system that Araceli described in "Bringing Designed Ideas to the Masses"?

8. Conduct a life cycle analysis of an automobile. (List all of the inputs and outputs associated with its production and use.)

9. What does the life cycle analysis of an automobile lead you to conclude about the unintended consequences of the automobile? How might engineers avoid unintended consequences using life cycle analysis?

## What Do You Think?

10. Dudley believes that engineers should understand all the processes in a system, no matter what aspect they are specifically involved in. Why do you think he believes this is important? What can this understanding do for the development of new processes and products?

# 8

## *The Making of a New Balance Shoe*

### Christine Epplett

Photo taken by Rebecca Pierik

### Key Concepts
#### from Previous Chapters

4  CAD

6  Assembly Line

6  Batch Production

7  Systems

Some of you might not realize that designing and developing an athletic shoe is an engineering task. Those of you who play sports, however, know that shoes aren't just a fashion statement. Shoes can make or break your performance on the field or on the court. Shoes that don't fit well or are poorly designed can even lead to injury.

My name is Christine Epplett, and I've always been interested in sports and fitness. Growing up, I ran track and cross country and played basketball in high school. In college, I was a member of the track team and played all kinds of intramural sports. I majored in business and found a job in health care administration after I graduated.

But wearing a suit to work every day just wasn't my style. I missed being around athletes. That's why I went back to school to study biomechanics in graduate school.

Biomechanical engineers design products, taking into account the physical forces that act on the body. I develop running shoes for New Balance Athletic Shoe, Inc., a large shoe manufacturing company with factories in the United States and around the world. I absolutely love my job. It's exciting to go to a road race, a park, or the grocery store and see people wearing the shoes that I spend months designing. It's also satisfying to feel like I'm helping athletes improve their performance while reducing the risk of injury. And you know what? The dress code at New Balance is "business casual," which means I get to wear running shoes to work every day.

At New Balance, much like at IDEO, we work in teams. These teams are composed of market researchers, designers, biomechanical engineers (like me), and process engineers who specialize in knowing the ins and outs of making shoes.

The research and development cycle (R&D) starts when our marketing department identifies a need. They use market research analysis to understand what new shoe designs the public wants and will buy. Recently, our marketing team identified a target consumer who is younger and more fashion conscious. These young customers want good-looking shoes that don't skimp on performance or comfort. Marketers also suggest a price point. That is to say, they tell us what a customer is willing to pay. This price will influence the quality of the materials and the manufacturing processes we use.

As soon as the design team members understand the target audience, the price point, and the required features, they begin developing a style for the shoe. In this picture, we have what's called a "classic" design, which has been popular for a few seasons now. Our designers are working to update this look in different colors—perhaps greens, soft blues, and pinks—to appeal to a younger consumer.

After our designers come up with something visually appealing, biomechanical engineers make sure this beautiful design will actually fit the human foot—and fit it well! Manufacturing engineers then decide whether the shoe can be manufactured in one of our plants. I need to know all the details, such as what kinds of materials our manufacturing machines can process efficiently, what kinds of stitches our associates are trained to use, and how many individual pieces must be cut to make each shoe. Next time you look at a pair of sneakers, try to see where the separate pieces of fabric have been stitched together. Most athletic shoes require between twenty and thirty pieces of fabric. Sounds like a lot, doesn't it?

The "classic" look has been popular for years. We're updating the look with bold colors that will appeal to younger consumers.

Other members of our team use Computer-Aided Design (CAD) software to develop the **blueprint** of the shoe. We can use CAD to assemble the entire shoe on the computer, creating detailed two- and three-dimensional drawings more easily than we could with traditional drafting. Some CAD systems can even simulate the manufacturing processes to ensure that our factory's machines and processes can actually make the shoe. Even better, CAD allows engineers to test products before we make a prototype. By applying "virtual stress" to a shoe design, we can get a sense of how well a shoe will withstand day-to-day pounding.

## The New Balance Team

### Marketers
Identify the target customer.

### Designers
Create an attractive design with the customer in mind.

### Biomechanical Engineers
Determine if the shoe design will fit a human foot.

### CAD Team Members
Use computer software to further test the blueprint of the shoe.

### Manufacturing Associates
The people who will produce the shoes, create and test a prototype.

### Manufacturing Engineers
Determine how the shoe can best be manufactured in large quantities

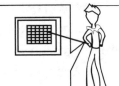

### Process Engineers
Are responsible for creating manufacturing systems and training the employees.

### Quality Control Personnel
Test shoes before and after they go to the market place.

After we've selected a design that meets all of our criteria and constraints, we create a list of specifications. The "specs," as we call them, detail exactly what materials are in the shoe and how the shoe must be made—from the color of the thread to the rubber in the sole. ***Manufacturing associates,*** skilled staff who actually produce the shoes, then use these specs to hand-stitch a prototype. One of my colleagues makes basketball shoe prototypes in his shoe size so he can wear them around, play basketball in them, and make sure they feel as good as they look. I do the same thing sometimes. We also ask athletes or sports enthusiasts to test our prototypes. They give us an unbiased opinion about comfort, performance, and style.

Prototypes often need to be modified. In this prototype, the "N" is off-center. We can't have that! Also, the ankle fits a little too snugly. These are common prototypes issues. We'll revise our specifications to resolve these two issues and, hopefully, in the next round the prototype will meet our requirements.

During the prototype stage, shoes are made in just one size. After we approve a prototype, we make the shoe in a variety of lengths and widths to check that the shoe pattern will fit a range of feet. After we determine that it will, our process engineers design patterns for every possible shoe size.

Finally, the design heads to the factory floor. The process engineers on our team have already prepped the manufacturing associates and set up the machines to make the shoe. Now we get to watch our best designs go into production. Soon, thousands of these shoes will be produced and shipped to a store near you.

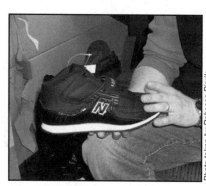

A prototype basketball shoe

## Beyond the Idea Stage: Production

We produce more than 4,000 shoes a day at our factory. That's around 900,000 pairs of shoes a year. It's an amazing number when you consider that we only have 225 manufacturing associates on the factory floor. Our success lies in how we've organized the factory. Believe me, we must design our factory systems as carefully as we design our shoes. Here is a simplified layout.

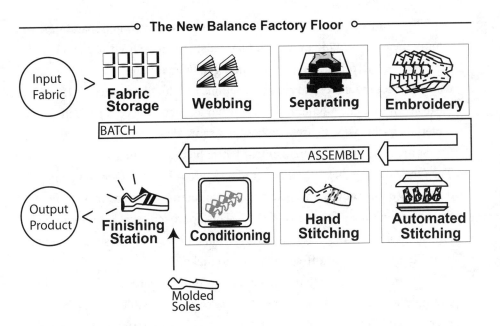

We start by batch producing the shoe parts. In a batch production system, associates create bunches of parts that will be assembled into larger products in a continuous production system. Let's talk about the steps in the manufacturing process.

## Separating

We start with large bolts of fabric. First, we cut the fabric into sheets, and then staple the sheets together, a process called webbing. We do this step so that the material can be processed in batches. Next we roll the batches of cut fabric into the die-cutting area. Here, associates use metal cutting dies, which work like cookie cutters, to cut materials into small pieces. The smaller the cutting dies are, the better we can line them up on the fabric without leaving big sections of uncut material.

To make a cut, an associate places a metal die along the fabric. Then a hydraulic press is used to apply pressure to the top of the die, which cuts through the webbed layers of fabric. Excess material is removed, leaving only the pieces that will go in to the shoes.

### Webbing

is the process of stapling sheets of fabric together.

### Separating

is the process of removing unwanted materials.

### Forming

is the process of using force to shape a material.

A cutting dye made by the forming process.

Those of us in the industry call this process *separating.* Separating simply means removing unwanted materials. If you've used scissors before, then you've had practice separating materials. Separating also refers to using heavier machinery to remove sections of a tougher material. If you've used a drill to make a hole in a piece of wood, then you've separated materials in this way. Chisels, lathes, and saws also separate materials.

Some shoe manufacturers cut all fabric pieces at a men's size 12 D. Then they remove the excess material and throw it away. Our company doesn't use this process. We use a whole collection of molds that range from women's size 5 to men's size 17. This approach takes a little more organization and time, but it saves material, and we feel it results in a better shoe fit. That's a trade-off we're happy to make.

We control every step of our separating process carefully. We offer our employees incentives to waste as little material as possible. We analyze every piece of cut fabric to ensure that most of the material we buy actually winds up in a shoe somewhere—maybe on your foot! And we resell any unused material to the factory from which we bought it. Those factories can recycle it into new fabric.

## Forming

We don't actually make our cutting dies. A company in Portsmouth, New Hampshire, makes them from high-carbon steel strips using a process called *forming.* Forming means using force to shape a material. Our dies are made with a press, which forms the strips into the cookie cutter–like shapes.

## Assembly

When all of the pieces are cut, they move on to the *assembly* stage of manufacturing. Our associates must sew most of the fabric pieces together using sewing machines. If you've ever used a sewing machine, then you know that this step takes a lot of time and labor. In an effort to boost efficiency, some of our associates use automated stitching machines to do some preliminary sewing.

These automated stitching machines work by casting a light that outlines the stitching pattern on the fabric pieces. The machine then takes a picture of the light and sends the images to a computer system. The system triggers another machine part to stitch along the path of light. These machines are extremely accurate and fast. They've helped us boost production a great deal.

After the machines complete the first stages of stitching, the rest of the stitching is done by hand. Skilled associates stitch fabrics with great precision. They don't use any guides to do this, just concentration and a steady hand.

Automated machines have led to the development of highly efficient manufacturing systems in recent years. In fact, some factories have grown so efficient that they don't use human laborers anymore. As a result, many people have lost their jobs to machines. Sure, these new technologies have led to greater profits for company owners. But at what cost to society? Many people now face unemployment and must get more training or education to find new work.

This is a trade-off that our owner, Jim Davis, is not willing to make. As a policy, Jim never lays off associates in exchange for making manufacturing processes more efficient. When we started using machines, associates were retrained to work in other parts of the factory. This approach costs the company money, but according to Jim, New Balance employees won't be as happy or as productive if they fear that their jobs may get cut the moment a new technology comes along. And no one will have an incentive to look for faster and better ways to make shoes if those improvements might jeopardize their jobs. Jim thinks that it's worthwhile to retrain associates or move them to other locations, and I think he's right. What do you think?

## Molding and Casting

As soon as the body of the shoe is stitched together, it's time to attach the sole. We aren't able to make all of our soles, so we have to buy some from a manufacturer in Asia who produces them based on our specifications. The soles are made using a process called *molding.* A mold is created in the size and shape of the sole, often out of plaster, then a liquid sole material is poured into a prepared mold (not unlike an ice cube tray) and allowed to solidify. After the sole material hardens, the finished sole is removed from the mold.

**Assembling** refers to the process of putting the parts of a product together.

Much of shoe assembly involves hand stitching.

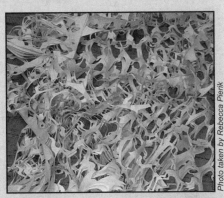

At New Balance, every piece of cut material is analyzed to ensure that we reduce fabric waste.

A machine automates the assembly process—but doesn't lead to job cuts at New Balance.

**Molding and casting**
is the process by which a material is liquified, poured into a mold of a desired shape, allowed to solidify in that shape, then removed from the mold.

**Conditioning**
refers to any process that uses high temperatures, chemicals, or mechanical force to change the properties of a material.

*Photo taken by Rebecca Pierik*

A conditioning machine uses heat to make a strong bond between a shoe and its sole.

**Finishing**
is any final treatment done to the surface of a product to make it more attractive to a consumer.

You'll sometimes hear manufacturing engineers use the term "casting" to describe a similar process to molding. In *casting,* however, the liquid material is a liquid metal or a ceramic instead of a plastic. Most ceramic dishes are made by casting, as are metal utensils and tools.

## Conditioning

We don't stitch our soles onto the shoes. They are glued on through an assembly process that uses chemical bonding adhesives. Stitches, on the other hand, are examples of mechanical fasteners—much like rivets, bolts, screws, nails, or staples.

Before applying the glue for the sole, the fabric must be treated to make it more pliable so that the adhesive sticks better. To do this, an associate places it in a machine that heats up the shoe and makes the fabric softer. In manufacturing lingo, we call this *conditioning,* which refers to any process that changes the properties of a material using heat, chemicals, or mechanical force. When you apply primer to a piece of wood before painting it, you're conditioning it, changing the wood's surface so that the paint goes on more smoothly. We heat condition our shoes so that the adhesive makes a stronger bond.

## Finishing

As soon as the shoes have soles, they are ready to be cleaned and laced—all part of the process of finishing. *Finishing* means any final treatment done to the product surface to make the product more attractive to a consumer. Finishing also describes the process of varnishing or lacquering a wooden chair, or glazing a ceramic bowl. We don't paint our shoes, of course, but we do clean off any scuffs, as well as excess glue or thread that may have accumulated during the manufacturing process. Finally, the shoes are boxed and ready to go to our distribution center.

*Engineering the Future: Science, Technology, and the Design Process*

# Quality Control

Before any batch of shoes can leave our factory, the shoes must pass stringent quality tests. Our quality control inspector, Ada Cardoza, is in charge of quality control on the factory floor. Ada roams the factory choosing three sample shoes at random from any finishing table. She measures the shoe's heel, the tongue, and the toe; she looks for any visible flaw in the material; she tugs at the sole and yanks on the laces. If she finds any defects in these random samples, the whole batch must be checked thoroughly. We use bar codes embedded in the fabric pieces to track exactly where the flaw originated in the manufacturing process. That way we can learn exactly what went wrong and correct the problem.

After a batch of shoes passes the quality control tests, it goes on to the distribution facility—a 259,000-square-foot warehouse that holds 2.4 million pairs of shoes at any given time. The distribution center receives shoes from the five New Balance factories in New England and combines them with inventory coming from several overseas factories. A constant flow of trucks picks up the shoes and delivers them to retail stores across the United States and Canada where you, the consumer, can buy them.

That's the story of how a new shoe goes from an idea in someone's mind to your foot. It's an incredibly complex route—and we're improving on it all the time. Ultimately, you, the consumer, get to judge how well our system works. The more "Ns" you see walking around your town, the better we're doing!

Ada Cardoza (right), who's in charge of quality control on the factory floor, and her colleague Leslie Castillo.

## What's the Story?

1. Chris discussed seven manufacturing processes: separating, forming, assembling, molding and casting, conditioning, finishing, and quality control. What are these processes, and how is each process used in the New Balance factory?

2. What's a trade-off? What is one trade-off that the New Balance management makes?

## Connecting the Dots

3. What processes in the New Balance factory involve batch production, and what processes involve assembly line–style production?

4. Robert Hartmann talked a lot about the importance of teamwork. Who are the members of the team involved in R&D at New Balance? Are they all engineers?

5. How do some engineers at New Balance test prototypes?

## What Do You Think?

6. You've just been hired as a consultant to a factory that makes wooden birdhouses. List the seven manufacturing processes mentioned in the chapter, and write how each process might be used in the factory.

7. You've just been hired as a consultant to a second factory. This factory makes ceramic coffee mugs. List the seven manufacturing processes mentioned in the chapter, and write how each process might be used in this factory.

# 9

# *Like Nature Intended*

## Saul Griffith

### Key Concepts
#### from Previous Chapters

1. Patent Research
2. Defining the Problem
2. Researching the Problem
8. Molding and Casting

If you think about it, nature can be a better manufacturer than humans. In fact, I'm disappointed with a lot of the things we mass produce. Take, for example, two manufactured products you commonly see: a plastic fork and a Styrofoam™ cup. Both take entire factories to produce, they function well for only one or two uses, and they last for hundreds or thousands of years in a landfill somewhere. This is not my idea of great design.

Nature, on the other hand, creates incredibly cool stuff right on the spot. A plant leaf, for instance, will hold together better than a lot of man-made materials. A plant can produce a leaf when it needs a new one. The plant doesn't have to make a thousand leaves and store them for later use. Nor does the plant need to go to a leaf supermarket to buy new leaves. The plant needs a leaf, so it gathers the raw materials from the soil, water, and air, and makes one right then and there—very simple. Elegant even. When the leaf degrades, it returns nutrients to the soil.

The plant needs a leaf, so it gathers the raw materials from the soil, water, and air, and makes one right then and there—very simple. Elegant even. When the leaf degrades, it returns nutrients to the soil.

My name is Saul Griffith, and I've been working for a few years on devising manufacturing systems that work more like Mother Nature. Recently, I designed a desktop machine that makes low-cost, high-quality eyeglasses for people in developing countries. The machine produces the glasses on demand, so there's no need for costly inventories or distribution systems.

I didn't grow up with the goal of making new and improved eyeglasses. I studied materials engineering at the University of South Wales in Sydney, Australia. Materials engineers specialize in knowing the structure and properties of different materials. We use this knowledge to envision new materials or new ways to use existing materials.

Engineers are always developing new materials or finding new ways to use materials already in existence. All materials fit into three categories: composite materials, natural materials, or synthetic materials. **Composite materials** are materials composed of at least two other materials. The properties of a composite are often more desirable than the properties of its individual components. For instance, fiberglass is made from glass and a plastic. The glass makes the plastic stronger and stiffer. Concrete, another composite, is made from sand, cement, and ground rock. **Synthetic materials** refer to materials that chemists design in a laboratory. When people talk about synthetics, they usually mean plastics. Plastics come in all varieties these days, from polyethylene sandwich bags to the polypropylene socks that keep your feet warm in the winter. Synthetics are remarkably versatile and show up in electronics, clothing, automobiles, and furniture—you name it. Do you own any rayon shirts or polar fleece jackets? These are made from synthetics. Of course, some products are made from **natural materials** such as leather, cotton, gold, and plant leaves.

**Composite materials** are made up of two or more different materials. The properties of a composite are more desirable than the properties of its individual components.

**Synthetic materials,** such as plastics, are created by chemists.

After I received my bachelor's degree, I began working on a project to build bridges out of glass composites. It was a worthwhile project, but I knew it would take a very long time to complete, so I began to look for other projects. I wanted to develop ideas and create designs that people could use every day.

I moved to the United States and enrolled at MIT as a doctoral student to work on a project developing electronic books. These electronic books would look and feel just like "real" books but would have pages that change on command, just like a computer screen. They would have enough memory to store a whole library, and they'd be cheap. That way people who didn't usually have access to books could have a whole library with just a single device!

In most developing countries, as well as in the United States, many schools can't afford to buy the books they need for their students. I wanted to change that, and I thought a new approach to manufacturing electronics might be a way to do it. I started designing a machine, something like a printing press, which "prints" transistors for computer chips onto large sheets of plastic.

When I presented my work to some visiting dignitaries from Kenya, they shocked me with their response. They told me that it would be nice if I found a way to get my electronic books to schools there. However, they cautioned, a quarter of the students wouldn't be able to read the books due to uncorrected eyesight problems.

Poor eyesight? I hadn't even thought of that! I know that glasses are expensive here, but I didn't realize that thousands of people all over the world suffer from poor vision and cannot afford eyeglasses at all. The World Health Organization estimates that as many as one billion people need glasses!

That's when I learned about a few students from Harvard Business School who were starting an interesting business venture—a company that produces low-cost eyeglasses for people in developing countries. They had done some research into the problem and found that only about half of the people who need glasses can afford them. These business students were looking for an engineer to help figure out how to develop a solution to this serious problem. I wanted to help and gladly joined their efforts.

## The Problem with Inventory

Before trying to design less-expensive eyeglasses, I did some research into why eyeglasses cost so much in the first place. To make a lens, the lens material (usually a plastic called "acrylic") is poured into a metallic or glass mold that gives the lens the correct shape. The acrylic is cheap, but the molds cost a tremendous amount of money to make. Manufacturers must make thousands of different molds for every different possible lens shape, which adds to the expense. In the United States, eyeglass retailers buy thousands of lenses at a time and store them as inventory. In some cities, you can walk into an eyeglass store and get new glasses in about an hour. You just hand your prescription to the clerk who plucks the appropriate lenses out of a vast inventory. The clerk grinds the edges of the lenses to fit your frames, and, voila, you walk out with your glasses one hour later.

But in remote areas of developing countries, people cannot afford to create and maintain an inventory of thousands of lenses for a relatively small population. Given how many different combinations of vision problems people can have, an inventory of 6,000 lenses would be required to guarantee that the store had the right lenses for just 200 people. Buying and maintaining 6,000 different lenses is very expensive, and stores must pass some of that expense on to the customer, driving the price of eyeglasses higher.

After learning about all of these issues, I realized I needed to design a manufacturing system that could produce lenses at a very low cost. Additionally, the system would have to eliminate the need for large inventories.

This wasn't the first time a manufacturing engineer had faced the inventory problem. In the 1950s, Japanese automakers could not afford to buy land to house huge inventories of cars, so they retooled their factories to produce cars on demand. Instead of producing as many cars as possible and then trying to sell them, companies such as Toyota and Honda started producing cars only after buyers had purchased them. As a consequence, these companies did not have huge inventory costs, and they seldom faced the problem of making cars they couldn't sell. Since then, factories all over the world have tried to incorporate *Just-In-Time* manufacturing, as it came to be called, into their factory design.

But some systems, such as eyeglass manufacturing and distribution, have been slow to change. I researched old patents to see if I could find out if anyone had ever tried a different approach. My search led me to liquid-filled lenses patented as early as the 1850s. These lenses were made of two sheets of thin glass with liquid pumped between them. The glass and liquid combination worked on the same principles that modern glass lenses do. The lenses bend light passing through them so that the light hits the wearer's eye directly on the retina. This lens allows the viewer to focus on objects that normally appear fuzzy or distorted.

These liquid-filled glasses wouldn't work for my purposes. They didn't look good and they couldn't correct all vision problems. I wanted to make glasses that looked good and, more importantly, worked as well as any you could get in the United States.

But I couldn't shake the idea of the liquid-filled lenses that could be adjusted into different shapes. Soon after, I turned that idea on its head. I could create a liquid mold that could be shaped and reshaped to create a lens to match practically any prescription, eliminating the need for multiple molds and large inventories. Inspired, I eventually developed a machine that makes lenses of any size and shape in about three minutes.

I made these two lenses and the lenses in my own eyeglasses using my machine.

Liquid acrylic is poured into a mold made of two membranes. Then two syringes pump baby oil into the membranes, changing their shape. When a desired shape is reached, an ultraviolet light and fan cool the acrylic until it hardens.

Photo taken by Rebecca Pierik

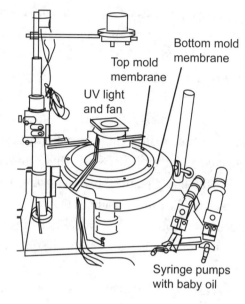

Top mold membrane

Bottom mold membrane

UV light and fan

Syringe pumps with baby oil

## Taking Another Look at the Problem

My new machine makes lenses quickly and the machine, or printer, is portable and inexpensive. People anywhere can afford to buy and use it. In addition, I've found frame suppliers that sell frames for under a dollar each. Problem solved. Right?

It's never that easy. Around the same time that I was building my lens-making device, one of my business partners was visiting India doing some more research into the issue. In the city of New Delhi, he found glassmakers who had had started a small business venture out of grinding lenses. The lenses worked relatively well, and they were cheap enough for most people to afford. Still, many people had uncorrected vision because they could not afford to have their eyes checked by an optometrist and they had no idea what kind of prescription they needed! After looking into this issue a little more, we realized that our eyeglass printer was only a partial solution.

So I began to develop a new system for diagnosing vision problems. Again, I started by researching the problems with the current system. I found that to get a prescription, you need an optometrist with five or more years of training or an expensive machine called an autorefractor. Not only do autorefractors cost a lot of money, they are also fragile and error-prone. For them to work, a patient must look at an electronic image a few inches away from his or her face. Most people have trouble focusing on such close-up images. As a result, these machines often misdiagnose a patient's eyesight.

To solve this problem, I've been developing a pair of diagnostic goggles. An electronic sensor superimposed on the goggles monitors the lens in the wearer's eye and adjusts the device's lens automatically to correct vision errors. To operate the goggles, patients must only hold the device and look through it. The goggles, once developed, should be cheap, easy to use, and they won't require an optometrist for basic prescriptions. I'm planning to test a new prototype this year.

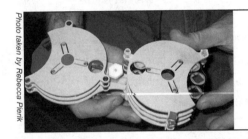

Photo taken by Rebecca Pfenik

This is the original prototype of the diagnostic goggles I'm developing. These goggles are cheap, and you don't have to be an optometrist to use them.

## Money Makes the World Go Round

I've been getting a lot of attention for my various inventions, and I have to say, it makes me uncomfortable. My desktop eyeglass printer has shown up on CNN, ABC, and in countless newspapers and magazines. But it's not finished yet! I've made one machine that works perfectly about 80 percent of the time; I need to make about a thousand machines that work perfectly 99 percent of the time before trying to distribute them to developing countries. Basically, I need to *optimize* my lens manufacturing system. I'm still trying to get more funding to do that, but it's not easy.

Researchers get funding from the federal government, private companies, or from foundations that provide grants. But before these institutions give you money, you must convince them that the problem is worth solving. These organizations tend to want to spend their money on American problems. It's not easy to get funding to work on solutions for developing countries. Most people in the United States don't understand the need for low-cost eyeglasses because it's not a widespread problem here.

Other factors make communicating my solution even more difficult. Many countries restrict companies that want to bring in new technologies like low-cost eyeglasses or diagnostic goggles. Indonesia, for example, has a law that makes it illegal for foreigners to provide eyeglasses to citizens there. That's strange, isn't it? Not all nations have these laws, but many countries do have laws that seriously limit the number of people an invention can help.

Still, I can reach some countries, such as India and Honduras. As soon as I've got my system working well enough, I'm going to do my best to get the glasses distributed in those countries. In the meantime, I'm going to complete my Ph.D. and put the finishing touches on a comic book series I'm writing about how to make cool stuff like skateboards that can slide over ice or duct-tape T-shirts that enhance your muscles. After that, who knows? I'm sure I'll never be at a loss for neat things to invent. For an engineer like me, the natural world provides abundant inspiration.

I'm writing a comic book series called *Howtoons* that explains how to make cool stuff.

## What's the Story?

1. You could say that Saul's motives were consistent throughout his career, but his engineering goals changed. What were his motives? How did his engineering goals change as he told his story?

2. Saul Griffith starts the chapter with the idea that nature is a better manufacturer than humans. Explain what he means. Give an example that's not in the chapter.

3. What is "Just-In-Time" manufacturing, and what are its advantages?

4. List two kinds of composite materials, two kinds of synthetic materials, and two kinds of natural materials.

5. How did Saul research the eyeglass problem and develop possible solutions?

## Connecting the Dots

6. Manufacturing systems don't just involve making a product. They also involve getting the product to the people who will use it. How does the inventory of New Balance Shoes in a sporting goods store compare to the inventory of lenses in an eyeglasses store?

7. Does Saul follow the steps of the design process in order? Which steps did he repeat? Which steps does Saul still need to complete?

## What Do You Think?

8. Saul Griffith is clearly motivated by the desire to help people in developing countries, not just to make money. Yet he says that money is very important. What does he mean by this? Why is money so important in engineering?

9. Why might countries restrict companies that want to bring in new technologies such as low-cost eyeglasses or diagnostic goggles?

# Sustainable Cities

# 10

# *Redesigning America*

## Peter Park

*Courtesy of Peter Park*

**Key Concepts**
**from Previous Chapters**

**2** Engineering Design Process

**7** Systems

City planners face many challenges. In regions with rapidly growing populations, people are becoming more and more dependent on automobiles. At the same time, "cookie-cutter" subdivisions often isolate people from the greater community. But with these problems come opportunities. In these new growth areas, more and more workers are adding to the economy. Many older, established American cities have museums, theaters, and universities. These offer diverse cultural experiences. In all cities, young and old, city planners are busy working to improve their conditions.

I'm Peter Park, and I oversee city planning in Denver, Colorado. Denver is a city that has grown quickly in recent decades, and today it faces a number of complex challenges and opportunities. I'm a part of a growing movement among urban planners, architects, developers, engineers, economists, and concerned citizens called New Urbanism. **New Urbanism** is an urban design movement that began in the late 1980s and early 1990s. New Urbanists aim to reform how our cities grow and to rebuild our regions, cities, towns, and villages. New Urbanism promotes neighborhoods that are walkable and include a diverse range of places to live, work, shop, and relax. We support regional planning of open space, architecture, and balanced development of jobs, housing, and transportation. We also believe that urban strategies are the best way to save the time people spend in traffic, to increase the supply of affordable housing, and to rein in urban sprawl. Many other issues, such as historic preservation, safe street design, and environmentally friendly building design, are also a part of the New Urbanism philosophy.

The New Urbanism approach certainly helped improve life in Milwaukee, Wisconsin, where I was the planning director from 1995 to 2004. I worked for a visionary leader, Mayor John Norquist (now President and CEO of the Congress for the New Urbanism). Together we improved the city's downtown, neighborhoods, and the river and lakefront areas by using New Urbanist principles. We even demolished an elevated downtown freeway. This provided opportunities for new development and improved connections to nearby neighborhoods. Replacing the elevated freeway with a walkable boulevard actually improved traffic circulation. It also removed a freeway that was both in the way and costly to maintain.

Now I oversee city planning in Denver, Colorado. As in Milwaukee, it's my job to guide Denver's development in a direction that makes it a more beautiful, enjoyable, and healthy place to live, work, and play.

I've always loved urban environments. Though I grew up in a small town, I remember traveling with my family to cities like Chicago, Boston, and New York. The beautiful buildings, parks, subways, and busy life on the street fascinated me and made a big impression. These experiences opened my eyes to how the design and structure of a community provides the setting for how people live.

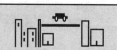

**New Urbanism**
is a movement among urban planners, architects, engineers, residents, and city officials to solve some of the design problems of modern American cities.

I grew up in Pierre, the capitol city of South Dakota. I remember riding bikes and walking with friends through the city's small downtown, past the beautiful historic courthouse, the Carnegie Library, and the capitol building and grounds. Whether large or small, a city's design plays a very important role in shaping civic pride and creating a sense of place.

I studied architecture in college. After working at architectural firms for a few years, I decided to pursue a master's degree in architecture at the University of Wisconsin. Several of my professors gave me the opportunity to work on projects much bigger than a single building. I became intrigued with urban planning and the overall structure of cities. Cities are much more than collections of buildings. Cities can actually have a life of their own, constantly growing to meet ever-changing needs. City planning requires not only an understanding of building and environmental design, but also economics, sociology, and politics. At the heart of the New Urbanism movement lies the concept of sustainable development. *Sustainable development* means directing the growth of a city so that it meets the needs of current residents without compromising the needs of future key elements. These elements are density, mixed-use environments, beautifully designed buildings and public spaces, and multi-modal transportation (cars, trains, subways, bicycles, and walking). And all this will benefit people now and for centuries to come.

> *Sustainable development* means directing growth so that it meets current needs without compromising future needs.

## The Elements of a Successful City

Like any large-scale project, redesigning a city is not only challenging, it's also an incredibly complex task. However, there are plenty of famous cities that work well: New York City, San Francisco, Montreal, and Paris, to name only a few. These cities are some of the most attractive and prosperous designed places on Earth. Tourists flock to these urban areas, and their high property values prove that people will pay a lot to live in them.

It's no secret what makes these cities successful. All of them share the same important elements. You don't have to live in Paris or Manhattan to enjoy good urban design. Any city or town, no matter what size or location, can be designed to incorporate some of the following: high density, mixed-use environments, beautiful buildings, beautiful spaces, and multi-modal transportation.

| Population Densities |
| --- |
| **Manhattan:**<br>$\dfrac{1.5 \text{ million people}}{23 \text{ square miles}}$<br><br>≈ 65,000 people/square mile |
| **Atlanta:**<br>$\dfrac{420,000 \text{ people}}{131 \text{ square miles}}$<br><br>≈ 3,200 people/square mile |

**Population density** refers to how many people a given space contains.

**Zoning laws** are laws that govern how land can be used and what attributes the structures on the land can possess.

# High Density

The great cities I just mentioned all have large populations, yes, but their populations are contained in a relatively small amount of space. Consider Manhattan, in the heart of New York City. Manhattan has a population of 1.5 million people living on approximately 23 square miles of land. That means that, on average, more than 65,000 people live on a square mile of Manhattan![1]

What are the advantages of a high-density city? **High density** reduces problems such as habitat destruction. Atlanta is a sprawling suburb with this problem. If the 1.5 million residents of Manhattan lived in city as dense as Atlanta, which has about 3,200 people per square mile, they'd take up about 470 square miles. That's a lot more habitat destruction.[1] It's fine that the natural habitats around cities like New York City or Paris have been paved over. However, the destruction is much less for each person in a city than a suburb or even a city with a less dense population.

High density has other advantages as well. Why is Manhattan such an exciting place to be? It's great for people watching! You can observe people from all ages and all walks of life—not to mention a few movie stars—coming together to do business and socialize. The city's "buzz" makes residents and visitors feel connected to the pulse of the community. It also gives people insight into other cultures and ways of living.

# Mixed-Use Environments

In densely populated cities, people live, work, play, and shop in the same area. When you walk through a city like San Francisco, you see storefronts, cafes, offices, and apartments all in one building. San Francisco has zoning laws that permit this type of mixed use. Other cities separate residential, commercial, and industrial areas. **Zoning Laws** are regulations that govern how land and the structures on them can be used. Zoning laws also dictate how tall a building can be, how far from other structures, and a variety of other restrictions.

---

[1]Source: US Census Bureau, 2000

Mixed-use zoning offers many advantages. Residents can walk to work, the store, or the park, which reduces automobile traffic, and this reduces traffic congestion and pollution. At the same time, residents get plenty of exercise. The average New Yorker, for instance, may walk four or five miles a day. You don't have to visit the gym after school or work if you walk that much!

## Beautiful Buildings

People travel thousands of miles to visit cities that have beautiful architecture. Museums, churches, and even corner stores in Paris are located in beautiful and often centuries-old structures that have been lovingly restored over the years. Of course, Paris and other large cities have modern architecture, too, but the modern buildings are designed to look good, work well as public spaces, and integrate nicely with the surrounding buildings.

Single buildings can house coffee shops, art galleries, and apartments, a reflection of multiple-use zoning laws.

I believe that every city has the potential to be as postcard-worthy as Paris. Many American towns and cities have historical structures. These structures could be restored into beautiful spaces that preserve the town's history and character. Even an old barn or factory warehouse in a town center can become a town hall or shopping mall. Restoring old structures also benefits the environment because it conserves lumber and other construction materials. You can think of it as a form of recycling!

You don't need an old building to preserve the charm and character of a city or town, though. Even tall skyscrapers don't have to appear cold and corporate. These buildings, when designed appropriately for multiple uses, can contribute to the look and character of a city.

## Beautiful Spaces

People want to feel connected to their communities. They like to go to central places where they can visit with friends, learn about local issues, and catch up on gossip. Great cities have public meeting places incorporated into their designs. These spaces may take the form of green parks, such as Central Park in New York or the Boston Common in Boston.

St Basil's Cathedral in Moscow

A walkable boulevard or "Main Street" can serve as a public space—as can a central building or a civic center. As long as it is free, pleasant, open to the public, easily accessible, and centrally located, any place can serve as a public meeting space.

## Multi-Modal Transportation

World-class cities provide people with a variety of transportation. Many cities use train and subway systems that shuttle people across town or to and from the suburbs. Public transit (buses, streetcars, trains, and subways) is a great investment. It reduces traffic and air pollution and promotes better land use. Transportation hubs, which promote pedestrian traffic, are excellent locations for retail businesses, restaurants, and public meeting spaces.

Many neighborhoods exclude walking and cycling in their designs. That's because the roads in many cities are for cars and are not very "people friendly." Great cities have streets that accommodate everyone, whether they use a wheelchair, a bicycle, or a just a pair of walking shoes. Well-planned sidewalks and bike lanes give pedestrians and bicyclists plenty of room. Well-designed crossing signals actually work, and motorists obey them!

Safe streets require more than proper signs and signals. Successful urban squares and streets are like "outdoor rooms." The buildings, sidewalks, lamps, benches, and cafes invite everyday contact, encourage an open exchange of ideas, and add to a city's vitality.

## Sprawl: The New Urbanist's Worst Enemy

We know what works, and we know what doesn't work: urban sprawl. *Urban sprawl* is a term that describes the rapid expansion of a city toward low-density surrounding areas. Urban sprawl occurs when rural land is developed faster than necessary to support population growth. As these areas are developed, farmland and natural habitats disappear, while developed areas, often in the city center, are abandoned. This population movement has been the predominant growth pattern in most American cities since World War II.

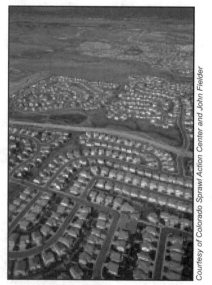

A bird's-eye view of sprawling development north of Denver

This unplanned sprawl resulted in a wasteful consumption of natural resources and other consequences. "Single-use" zoning laws that separated residential, commercial, employment, and recreation areas forced residents to travel long distances, which led to wide use of automobiles. This lifestyle led to the traffic congestion and pollution that most of us confront every day. Those unable to drive—the young, disabled, and the elderly—still face significant disadvantages.

## Denver's Challenge and Opportunity

Denver has suffered some of the negative consequences of urban sprawl and continues to deal with growth pressures. During the 1990s, Denver's population grew by 87,000 people—an 18.6 percent increase. And it continues to grow. By 2020, we anticipate a population growth of an additional 132,000 people. The population is expected to grow by one million people by 2025. Current estimates predict that land development will to continue to expand, consuming thousands of acres of rural land. Most of the roadways will be operating at or over capacity.

The expected growth in Denver can be seen as either a threat or an opportunity. Fortunately, people in Denver are now dedicated to sustainable long-term city planning and are willing to invest in the city's future. Voters recently approved a $4.7 billion plan to expand our light-rail and bus transit system. Called FasTracks, the project will connect the new with the old, providing people with alternative transportation from the inner city to suburban areas. What's more, we expect FasTracks to stimulate the growth of new urban centers around the city.

The idea is to reduce urban sprawl and create exciting new places to live, work, and play. Imagine stepping off a train after school or work to find a lively central plaza. You are surrounded by stimulating architecture. You walk past a scene of open-air markets and cafes. Restaurants and businesses are at street level and apartments and offices are on the upper stories. The plaza gives way to a tree-lined boulevard along which pedestrians and cyclists safely move in dedicated lanes alongside the streets.

This is Denver's "New Urbanist" vision—exactly the kind of scene that would look great on a postcard! Now, doesn't that beat sitting in traffic?

## What's the Story?

1. What is New Urbanism?

2. What does the term "sustainable development" mean? Give three examples of development that might be considered sustainable.

3. Why does Peter say that Denver's path of development was not sustainable? What is the solution he is working on?

4. How does urban sprawl harm the environment? What are some other problems with sprawl?

5. What are multiple-use zoning laws? In Peter's opinion, how do multiple-use zoning laws benefit a city?

## Connecting the Dots

6. What does urban sprawl have to do with the unintended consequences of the automobile that Araceli Ortiz described in Unit 1?

7. After FasTracks is implemented, will Denver's development problems be solved once and for all? Using what you learned about the design process from Shawn Frayne and Jamy Drouillard, explain your answer.

## What Do You Think?

8. Every design can be improved upon. Think about your own city or town. What are its major design problems? Write a list of at least three problems and describe what impact these problems have on your community.

9. Prescribe New Urbanist solutions to the problems you identified in your previous answer.

10. Do you believe that the New Urbanism approach is the best approach to urban planning? Why or why not?

# *Bridging the Future*

## Kirk Elwell

Photo taken by Benjamin T. Erwin

### Key Concepts
from Previous Chapters

2 Engineering Design Process

9 Materials

10 Cities and Towns, Designed Systems

The Central Artery/Tunnel Project is one of the largest and most technologically challenging highway projects in American history. The goal is to improve the traffic flow in Boston, Massachusetts, by changing the Central Artery, a large section of an above-ground highway, into an underground tunnel.

I'm Kirk Elwell, a lead field engineer working on the Central Artery/Tunnel Project, often dubbed the "Big Dig." When the original Central Artery opened in 1959, it carried about 75,000 vehicles a day without any problems. But as the number of people using this stretch of highway nearly tripled, it became one of the most congested highways in the country. Accident rates were nearly four times the average for urban interstates.

The situation was only going to get worse. Researchers estimated that by 2010 the deteriorating Central Artery would hold traffic at a stop-and-go pace for sixteen hours a day unless a solution was found. What's more, the Central Artery ran right through the busiest shopping and dining district in the city. The unsightly highway was bad for business.

Since construction began in 1991, we have created a tunnel under the Boston Harbor. This tunnel connected Boston to the airport, built new connections to the highway from formerly inaccessible parts of town, and sunk much of the Central Artery below ground. One end of the Central Artery tunnel meets with the Leonard P. Zakim Bunker Hill Bridge, which opened to traffic in 2003. This bridge crosses the Charles River, connecting the city of Boston with surrounding suburbs. But beyond moving traffic, the bridge designers planned for it to become a city landmark—not unlike San Francisco's Golden Gate Bridge or St. Louis's Arch.

Even though our tax dollars are paying for the Big Dig, I don't work for the government. I work for Bechtel/Parsons Brinckerhoff, a company that was hired by state and federal government agencies to provide the engineering design and construction management for everyone from bricklayers and welders to carpenters and other technicians. This collaboration allows for better communications between management, engineers, and the construction crews on the job site.

As a field engineer, my usual "office" is the job site. I enjoy being outside and active, so this job is "right up my alley," so to speak. A structural engineer may spend a good deal of time in front of a computer calculating the structural forces of a bridge or tunnel. Field engineers spend most of their day ensuring that the job is being done right. Sure, I might spend a few hours at my desk looking at engineering and architectural plans, but unlike a structural engineer, I put my engineering skills into supervising and troubleshooting on the job site.

The Leonard P. Zakim Bunker Hill Bridge

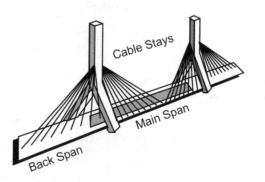

Cable Stays

Main Span

Back Span

The process of designing the Zakim Bridge has been an interesting mix of architecture and engineering. After the site for the bridge was decided, the Federal Highway Administration asked several architects to draw possible designs for the bridge. Architects tend to specialize in the form of structures. Sure, they need to have a good sense of whether or not their design can actually be built. But, in general, architects focus more on how the structure will look and how people will interact with it. After an architect designs the plans, a structural engineer will make sure that the structure can withstand the forces of weather, traffic, people, or any other force that might act on it.

Christian Menn, a Swiss architect and engineer, submitted the winning design. The structural engineers worked out the specifications for all of the bridge's components. It was their job to make the bridge look the way Mr. Menn designed it, while withstanding all of the required loads. Engineers often refer to the weight and forces that a structure must support as "loads." Loads are broken into two categories: dead loads and live loads. A *dead load* is any load associated with the structure itself—the road, steel beams, and concrete. A *live load* is any other force applied to the structure due to cars, people, wind, snow, earthquakes, and so on. Today, engineers use computers to model how structures will behave under certain loads. Still, it took one engineer many months to design the structure of the two towers so that they would be as narrow as the architect wanted. The towers had to be able to withstand the predicted loads and maintain their slim appearance.

The architect and the engineers also had to decide what materials to use for construction. Most bridges are made of steel and concrete. Steel is a great material for a bridge because it is very lightweight but very strong. In fact, a steel bridge can usually support a live load equal to its dead load. This means that if you had a steel bridge with a dead load of 25,000 tons, it could support a live load of another 25,000 tons. This would give you a total load of 50,000 tons. *Total load* is the sum of the dead load and the live load.

Dead Load + Live Load = Total Load

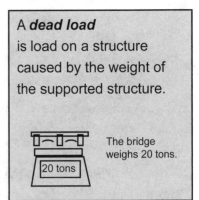

A *dead load*
is load on a structure
caused by the weight of
the supported structure.

The bridge
weighs 20 tons.

20 tons

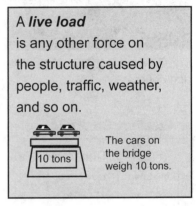

A *live load*
is any other force on
the structure caused by
people, traffic, weather,
and so on.

The cars on
the bridge
weigh 10 tons.

10 tons

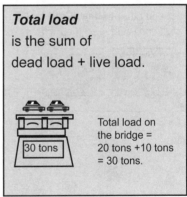

*Total load*
is the sum of
dead load + live load.

Total load on
the bridge =
20 tons +10 tons
= 30 tons.

30 tons

The Zakim is a hybrid of steel and concrete.

### Steel vs. Concrete

| Steel | Concrete |
| --- | --- |
| **Live Load** 25,000 tons | **Live Load** 25,000 tons |
| **Dead Load** 25,000 tons | **Dead Load** 75,000 tons |
| **Total Load** 50,000 tons | **Total Load** 100,000 tons |

A concrete bridge, on the other hand, can only carry a live load that is 25 percent, or one-quarter, of its total load. In order to carry a live load of 25,000 tons, the concrete bridge must have a dead load of 75,000 tons. That gives us a total load of 100,000 tons! The concrete bridge will be bigger and heavier. That's because concrete must be a lot thicker than steel to support the same live load.

It seems obvious that we'd build bridges out of steel, right? Actually, it's anything but obvious. Concrete, it turns out, is much less expensive than steel, and it's much easier than steel to maintain. Steel corrodes over time, but concrete will not. At the same time, concrete is fire-resistant, whereas steel will melt in a fire. Since the collapse of the World Trade Center Towers on September 11, 2001, we've had to be more careful about how public structures perform during fires. Engineers must consider a wide range of factors in addition to a material's strength.

We designed the Zakim Bridge to be a hybrid of both concrete and steel. That way we can get the best characteristics of both materials. We can also distribute the weight of the bridge more effectively with the hybrid design.

## The Great Balancing Act

Menn chose a cable-stayed design for the bridge. The design has two main towers. Both the north and south towers are on land, so we don't have to worry about boat traffic on the river. Cables from the two towers support the main span and the roadways leading to the bridge. The bridge is high enough off of the river that sunlight can easily reach the water.

So how do you design a bridge to carry 100,000 tons of concrete, steel, and traffic? The two towers hold the majority of the weight. The towers straddle the eight-lane roadway, and then rise nearly 300 feet into the air above the bridge. Each tower requires a strong underground foundation that anchors it in place. For the Zakim bridge, the crew sank shafts 140 feet below ground level—deep enough so that each shaft extends through solid bedrock.

These shafts allow the towers to withstand immense compression forces. *Compression* occurs when the ends of an object are being pushed toward each other. The cables that attach the towers to the roadway pull the tower down, while the ground pushes the towers up. As a consequence, the towers are under tremendous compression.

The cables themselves experience another force called tension. *Tension* occurs when the ends of an object are pulled away from each other. Just like a rope in a game of tug of war, the cables are pulled in one direction by the roadway and in the opposite direction by the towers.

It makes sense that we would hold up the part of the bridge over the water—called the main span—with cables. There's no other way to hold it up. But why do the cables support the roadway approaches that are over land, which we call the "back span"? Well, if we only attached the cables to the part of the bridge over the water, each tower would be pulled in toward the center of the bridge under the weight of the roadway. The towers would bend inward. This bending would occur due to one side of the tower being compressed and the other side being pulled in tension. So the back span acts as a counterweight, with the cable effectively pulling the towers out so that they do not bend in toward the main span. To improve the effectiveness, the back spans are made of heavier steel-reinforced concrete, while the main span is constructed with a more lightweight steel frame.

---

**Balancing the Bridge**

**Forces on the Bridge**

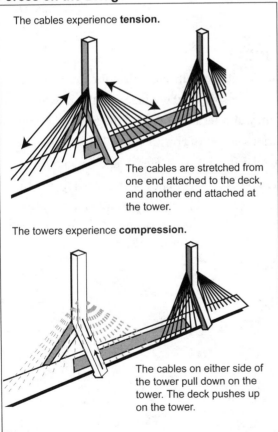

The cables experience **tension**.

The cables are stretched from one end attached to the deck, and another end attached at the tower.

The towers experience **compression**.

The cables on either side of the tower pull down on the tower. The deck pushes up on the tower.

**Parts of the Bridge**

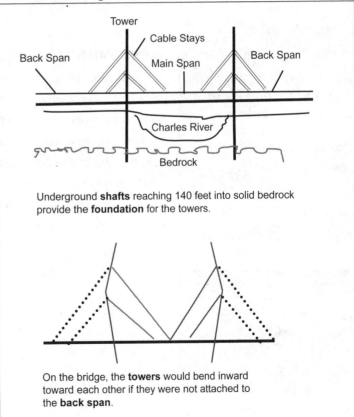

Tower

Cable Stays

Back Span          Main Span          Back Span

Charles River

Bedrock

Underground **shafts** reaching 140 feet into solid bedrock provide the **foundation** for the towers.

On the bridge, the **towers** would bend inward toward each other if they were not attached to the **back span**.

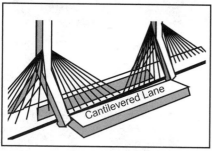

Cantilevered Lane

**Forces and Structures**

**Compression** occurs when the ends of an object are pushed toward an object's center.

**Tension** occurs when the ends of an object are pulled away or stretched from its center.

**Bending** is when one side of an object experiences tension and the other side experiences compression.

**Torsion** is a twisting force that results when one side of an object moves in a different direction than the other side.

As you can see, the bridge is a big balancing act! And the act would be much simpler if the bridge were perfectly symmetrical. But it's not. In addition to the main eight lanes, there are two additional lanes of traffic on the east side of the bridge. The extra lanes had to be built on the east because the bridge bumps up against a large sports stadium and a subway station on the west side. These lanes are cantilevered off of the main span. A *cantilever* refers to a part of a structure that projects into space supported only at one end. The cantilevered lanes are attached to the bridge on one side. The other side hangs freely over the river.

The weight of the extra two lanes throws the balance of the bridge off a bit, leading to torsion. **Torsion** is a twisting force that results when one side of an object moves relative to the other side. When you wring out a washcloth, the cloth is experiencing torsion as your hands twist parts of the cloth in different directions. Similarly, the weight of the two extra lanes causes the bridge to bend slightly. The bend is greatest at the center of the main span, while the back span remains fixed. As a result, the roadway experiences torsion (twisting force). Left uncorrected, the torsion could cause the roadway to fracture. To make the roadway safe for traffic, we moved the cable attachments on the tower a little bit off center to support the extra weight on the east side of the roadway, which prevents the main span from bending. We also made the cables on that side larger to bear the extra load of the additional lanes.

## Designing for Construction

Loads that occur during construction often are different than the loads after a structure is completed. Not only did the structural engineers of the Zakim Bridge test a scale model of the bridge, they also tested models of the finished bridge step by step, as it would be at various stages of construction. This was to make sure that the bridge could withstand different loads. Heavy equipment also produces a higher load than a structure will experience with everyday use. In addition, the effects of the wind might be different on a partially built bridge.

Temperature can also affect how construction materials behave during building. We got a lesson about that when we built the main span of the bridge. We first constructed the back spans of the bridge and then began building both sides of the main span from the towers out over the river. We attached the cables from the towers to each newly constructed section one-by-one as we progressed.

On an unusually warm May morning, we had reached the center of the main span, and the two sides of the main span were ready to be connected with a final piece of supporting steel. Our structural engineer calculated that the last piece of steel should be about 6' 7.5" long. We had the steel cut with precision instruments by a company in Colorado to ensure that it would be the correct length.

But on this hot, hot day, we found that the piece of steel was too long! That's because materials tend to expand as they get hotter and shrink as they get cooler. This phenomenon is referred to as *thermal expansion.* The steel cutters in Colorado knew that the steel piece would expand or shrink with temperature changes. They had calculated and cut the steel so its length would be just right at a temperature of about 50 degrees Fahrenheit, Boston's average springtime temperature.

That morning it was about 55 degrees, but by noon the temperature hit 90 degrees! The steel expanded so much that it jammed itself into the incorrect position between the two halves of the bridge! We needed to come up with a solution. One engineer suggested running cold water down the length of the beams to cool them down. We ran hoses and sprinklers all over the bridge. After fourteen hours, the steel finally shrank one inch. That was all we needed to move the beam to the correct position and bolt it into place as quickly as we could.

## Designing Relationships

Working as a field engineer isn't just about making things run smoothly on the job site. It's also about making sure that relationships with every organization involved with the construction of the bridge run smoothly. Sometimes managing these relationships can take a lot of time—and money! Most civil engineering projects involve many different organizations. The City of Boston, the Federal Highway Administration, Amtrak, a host of utilities companies, the Coast Guard, Boston's subway system, and workers' organizations are just a few of the groups involved in the Big Dig.

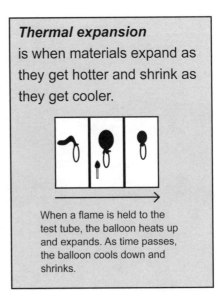

***Thermal expansion*** is when materials expand as they get hotter and shrink as they get cooler.

When a flame is held to the test tube, the balloon heats up and expands. As time passes, the balloon cools down and shrinks.

All of these groups influence how we do our work. For one section of the old highway that we are demolishing, we can only work between 1:30 and 4:30 A.M. We can only work when the subway is not operating, because debris could fall onto a moving subway train and injure passengers. The crew is only allowed to work these three hours each day, a total of fifteen hours a week. But because of labor laws, we have to pay them for forty hours a week. And during those hours, we can't make a lot of noise that could disturb the residents in nearby buildings, so we use more expensive equipment. It's very quiet, but it takes longer to complete the work. We've spent a lot of time and money taking this section of the highway down, but it's worth it. The city is happier with how we're getting the job done, so we feel it's a trade-off worth making.

The Big Dig is incredibly complex, but I like trying to figure out all of the different pieces. And I'm proud to be a part of such a historic effort. I've been working on the Big Dig for thirteen years—a long time for just one project—but when I think about the long-term impact of my work, thirteen years is really not so long. The Big Dig will make the roads safer and Boston more beautiful. That's good for tourism and business, and for everyone's quality of life. I feel very satisfied at the end of each day. And I get to work outside!

*Engineering the Future: Science, Technology, and the Design Process*

## What's the Story?

1. According to Kirk, what are the main problems that the Central Artery Project is trying to solve?

2. Three engineers are designing a civic center for a small city: an architect, a structural engineer, and a field engineer. Describe how each team member would contribute to the construction project. Name at least three other individuals who might also work on the project.

3. What were the design requirements of the Zakim Bridge?

## Designing with Math and Science

4. Describe at least three structural components that contribute to the dead load of your school building. Describe at least three components that contribute to the live load.

5. What is the minimum dead load (in tons) of a steel bridge that must carry 100 tons of traffic? What will be the total load of that bridge?

6. A scaffold has a dead load that is 60 percent of its total load. If the scaffold weighs 1,200 pounds, how much live load is it supporting?

7. Define compression and tension. Would the rope in a tug-of-war contest experience compression or tension?

8. Describe how bending occurs in a diving board with someone standing on the end. You may want to draw a sketch to help you.

## Connecting the Dots

9. In "The Art of Engineering," Robert Hartmann discussed how an object's "look and feel" is as important as its function. Would Kirk Elwell agree? Copy two or more sentences from this chapter that support your answer.

## What Do You Think?

10. Kirk talks about the importance of keeping relationships with other organizations running smoothly, even if it means spending more money on the project. What might the consequences be if engineers and managers working on the Central Artery Project ignored the interests of civic organizations? How does this relate to your own life? What relationships are important for you to keep running smoothly every day?

# 12

# *Tower in the Sky*

## Bill Baker

### ⚙ Key Concepts
#### from Previous Chapters

**11** Loads

**11** Bending, Compression, Tension

**11** Foundation

**11** Construction Materials—Characteristics

People have always wanted to build to the sky. More than 5,000 years ago, people pushed the available technology to its limits to build the monumental Pyramids of Egypt. Ancient towers and minarets dot the landscapes of Europe, the Middle East, and Asia. Today, the skyline of any modern city in America proves that we're still using the most advanced technologies to construct buildings that scrape the sky.

I'm Bill Baker, and I've made a career of designing super-tall structures. I'm a structural engineer at Skidmore, Owings, and Merrill LLP (SOM), a Chicago-based architecture and engineering firm. We are famous for our award-winning skyscraper designs. I'm currently working on plans for the Burj Dubai, a multi-use skyscraper in Dubai, a city in the United Arab Emirates, a small nation northeast of Saudi Arabia on the Arabian Gulf.

A perspective drawing of the proposed building design for the Burj Dubai

The Burj Dubai will be the tallest building in the world, with over 3,000,000 square feet of residential and commercial space. I can't tell you exactly how tall it will be—that's a closely guarded secret until the building is unveiled to the public in 2008. I can only tell you that the Burj Dubai will surpass the world's current tallest building, Taiwan's Taipei 100, which was completed in 2004, and is 1,671 feet. That's about one and a half times as tall as the Eiffel Tower in Paris.

Growing up in a small town in Missouri, I wouldn't have guessed that my job would take me across the world to nations such as China, Malaysia, or the United Arab Emirates. I didn't know any engineers when I was younger and I didn't really know what engineering was. In high school, I took an aptitude test to help me decide what I should do after graduation. I scored well in the math and science portions of the test, and my responses indicated that I enjoyed applying my math and science knowledge to create things. My guidance counselor told me the test results showed that engineering would be a good career choice. When I told my mother, she informed me that both of my grandfathers had been engineers. They had passed away before I was born, so I had never known them. I felt honored to be starting down a similar path to the ones they had taken.

In college and graduate school I became interested in large structures such as aircraft hangars and convention centers. Building big structures involves a complex and interesting set of constraints that I find challenging and exciting. First off, big structures have enormous live and dead loads, so they must support a lot of weight. Secondly, the skyscrapers must stand up during storms—and believe me, the higher you build, the stronger the force of the wind! Finally, these buildings are very expensive to build and require vast quantities of materials. So structural engineers must choose construction materials very carefully, balancing strength and cost.

# The Tallest Tower

To understand why we're building the world's tallest tower in Dubai, you need to know something about the place. In recent years, Dubai has experienced a period of unprecedented growth. New laws and regulations make it very easy and inexpensive for international companies to do business there. The city was transformed into an international melting pot. People from the Arab world, Asia, Africa, Europe, Australia, and the United States have moved there in recent years as a result of the booming economy. With luxury resorts, plenty of fine dining, and bustling shopping districts, the city has also become a popular tourist destination of wealthy Europeans and Americans. In fact, a "celebrity culture" like one you might find in Miami or Hollywood has started to take shape.

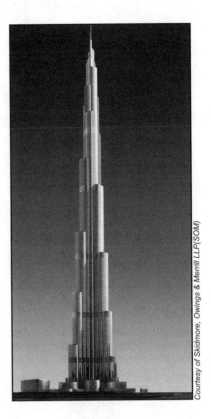

Courtesy of Skidmore, Owings & Merrill LLP (SOM)

In 2003, EMAAR Properties, a real estate development company in Dubai, asked my company to submit a proposal for a super-tall building. The company wanted a structure that would serve as an emblem of the city's prestige, something that would raise the stature of Dubai as a global tourist destination. Years ago, this is what the Eiffel Tower did for Paris and the Golden Gate Bridge did for San Francisco. A number of firms submitted designs, but we were chosen to design the new skyscraper.

Our design was inspired by a flower that is native to the region. The base of the Burj Dubai blossoms upward in a series of steps to give the tower a graceful transition from the ground. The design offers impressive views and protection against high winds. When complete, the tower's 160-plus stories will house a world-class hotel, luxury condominiums, and office spaces. The top stories will be used by telecommunications companies for satellite and radio transmissions. Whole floors will be reserved for building maintenance, where several cranes and drop baskets will be used for window cleaning and outside maintenance. The window-washing equipment alone will occupy several stories. The "skin," or outer covering, of the building will be made almost entirely of glass to allow for breath-taking views of the Arabian Gulf and the desert.

Windows make the walls of stone towers weaker and less structurally sound.

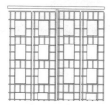

The steel frames of this metal-framed building carry the load.

## Rising Higher

Humans can only build as high as current technology permits. During the Middle Ages, massive stone walls supported towers and spires. The walls were very thick in order to support the dead load of the structure. Building a taller tower required that the lower walls be thicker to support the load of the walls above them. The Leaning Tower of Pisa, for example, has walls as wide as thirteen feet on the lower floors. There is a limit to how high you can build just by making the walls thicker. In towers above a certain height, the walls must be so thick that little open space remains inside. In addition, stone towers rarely have many windows, because they weaken the walls and the structural integrity of the buildings.

During the Industrial Revolution, engineers began experimenting with new ways to manufacture long beams of iron and steel. By the late 1800s, engineers designed buildings with metal frames. In these buildings, the steel frame, not the outer walls, carries the load of the structure. In these designs, the outer walls could have plenty of windows. In fact, the skyscrapers of the 20th century often had glass walls to allow for great views and plenty of natural light. And because steel is much lighter and stronger than stone, brick, or mortar, steel-frame buildings can rise much higher than earlier buildings, which seldom extended past ten stories.

## A Matter of Geometry

The frame of the building—its skeletal bones—keeps the structure standing despite very high loads. The shape of a building's frame can minimize the amount of tension or compression that every individual beam and column bears. How is this possible?

Let's look at a very simple frame with four joints, or corners, pictured below. If a force, perhaps wind, acts on this frame from the side, the top and bottom would slide past each other, causing shear. ***Shear*** is a force that results in the deformation of an object in which its parallel planes remain parallel but move past one another.

*Engineering the Future: Science, Technology, and the Design Process*

A tall structure such as a skyscraper may start to bend as shear increases. Remember, bending occurs when one side of an object experiences tension and the other side experiences compression. When bending becomes too great, the structure is in danger of toppling to the ground.

As you can imagine, engineers want to minimize the effects of bending as much as possible, because it reduces the stability of the frame. We can do this by adding diagonal members, forming a truss. A *truss* is a triangular arrangement of structural members that increases a structure's rigidity (shown on the right). When a shearing force pushes on the side of the frame, the truss holds the joints in place so they cannot slide apart. The entire structure resists the force, not just each individual column.

The Empire State Building, constructed with a steel frame in 1931, is a good example. The Empire State Building's strong frame allowed it to rise 1,250 feet into the air, making it the tallest building in the world until 1972. Its impressive height along with its beautiful design made the building an internationally celebrated landmark. But the building's steel skeleton, a three-dimensional grid of columns and beams, restricted its indoor space. In fact, most of floors are chopped up into small rectangular rooms, and the interior rooms get very little daylight.

Steel frames and truss systems are quite strong, but they are not the only way to make tall buildings stand up to the forces of nature. Nowadays, many buildings are constructed around a strong central core that supports the structure like a spine. This spine acts like a tall, wide column held together with trusses or walls. In many buildings the core is constructed around the elevator shafts, because they must be very straight.

Very tall structures are often designed with multiple elevators, requiring a wide core composed of many solid vertical columns. The floors of the building then span from the core to the columns at its sides. This allows for nice, open floor plans, large rooms, and plenty of natural light throughout the building.

> A *truss* is a triangular arrangement of structural members.

## Tall Building Constructed Around a Central Core

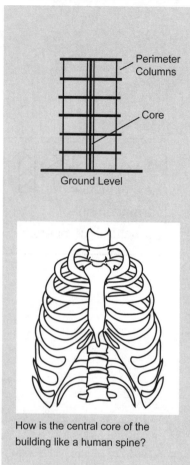

How is the central core of the building like a human spine?

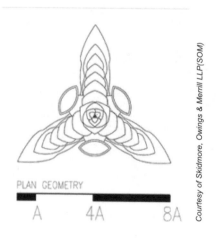

PLAN GEOMETRY

A    4A    8A

*Courtesy of Skidmore, Owings & Merrill LLP(SOM)*

Today, durable reinforced concrete is often used instead of steel for the columns and core walls. Concrete is a hard substance made from cement, crushed rock or sand, and water, which performs very well under compression forces. Modern concrete also uses fly ash from coal-fired power plants, ground up blast furnace slag from steel manufacturing, and silica dust from computer chip manufacturing as substitutes for some of the cement.

These waste products from other industries actually make concrete stronger and contribute to recycling. While concrete is very strong in compression, it doesn't resist tension forces very well. To make it perform better under tension or bending, concrete is reinforced with steel bars (called rebar). The reinforced concrete works just as well as steel for many purposes, and for compression elements such as columns, it is hard to beat.

While engineering the Burj Dubai, I've thought a lot about how to distribute the load while maintaining an open floor plan. After all, its dead load will be approximately a half-million tons. That's one billion pounds!

In our design, the central core and the perimeter columns are supported from deep underground. The underground portions of the columns are called piles. These piles act like the roots of a tree, adding even more stability. Each pile carries about 3,000 tons.

The central core of the Burj Dubai resembles the hub of a wheel with three spokes, which spread out into the three wings of the structure, so that the immense weight is distributed over all three wings of the building. In turn, each wing has its own walls along the corridors and perimeter columns. Each wing was designed to be a stable structure in and of itself. This wing design bolsters the support of the central core, allowing the Burj Dubai to reach its towering height.

## Confusing the Wind

The enormous load of a structure like the Burj Dubai actually comes in handy when battling the largest force that the building will have to withstand: the wind. Wind gusts can reach up to 160 miles per hour at the top of the spire. The mere weight of the building helps brace the structure against the wind. You can get a sense of this by placing two soda cans, one empty and one full, on a table top and aim a fan directly at them. Which soda can is more likely to remain standing? The full one, of course! That's because the full can's weight pushes the can onto the surface of the desk, stabilizing it.

*Engineering the Future: Science, Technology, and the Design Process*

But the building's load is not enough to withstand the extremely high forces that wind can produce. Wind acts on the building's surface in two different ways. It pushes directly on the side of the building to produce a force called "drag." Wind also swirls around the edges of the building, creating small "vortices," or whirlpools, of spinning air.

Though drag can get quite strong, it's really the force of the vortices that give us the greatest concern. When these forces develop at opposite sides of a building, they can actually push the building from side to side. If the vortices spin at exactly the right speed, they can intensify the building's natural swaying motion, causing it to rock back and forth dramatically.

If you have ever been to the top of a skyscraper, then you may have felt it swaying. To solve the wind problem, we purposely design skyscrapers so that they are flexible. They move a little with the wind and with the movements of the Earth. That's because even very small movements at the base are translated to larger movements at the top. If you hold a long fishing rod in your hand, you'll notice that the tip of it sways back and forth no matter how steadily you try to hold it.

A skyscraper's flexibility also makes it better able to withstand earthquakes. In an earthquake, a skyscraper rides the waves of the shaking Earth almost like a surfer. Even a smaller, more rigid structure that does not sway is more likely to fracture and collapse. It may seem unlikely, but you might be better off in a well-designed skyscraper than in a two-story building during an earthquake.

Every tall building sways from one side to the other and back again in a set number of seconds. The time it takes for one full cycle is called a **period**. The Sears Tower in Chicago, for instance, has a period of 7 and 3/4 seconds. The Burj Dubai will have a period of eleven seconds.

If the vortices at the edges of the building begin pulling the structure from side to side in rhythm with the natural period of the building, the building will began to sway a greater and greater distance from its vertical position. To understand how this happens, think of how you move back and forth on a swing. When you kick your feet in rhythm with the motion of the swing, each kick propels the swing higher and higher. When timed correctly, the relatively small force of kicking results in increasingly higher swings. Similarly, at certain speeds, the small forces of the vortices may cause a building to start rocking violently.

Even relatively small forces of the vortices may cause a building to start rocking dangerously to and fro.

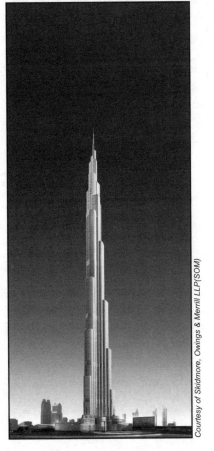

Courtesy of Skidmore, Owings & Merrill LLP(SOM)

All skyscrapers are designed to compensate for these forces. For the Burj Dubai, the design team varied the width of the building and the shape of the floors. Every section that has a different width or a different-shaped floor will have vortices occurring at different spinning rates. We changed the shape of the building 24 times in order to confuse the wind. It's as if you sat on your swing and kicked your left foot at one rate and your right foot at another. If you do that, the swing won't go very high. We tested each design by placing a scale model in a wind tunnel and observing how it behaved during a range of wind speeds. From wind-tunnel tests, we were able to identify the areas affected by vortices, and modify the design to reduce these forces.

Engineers can also "tune" a building to make sure that it has a period that is unlikely to become synchronized with the side-to-side pushing of the vortices. By analyzing data about storms and wind currents at the construction site, we determined the safest period for the structure. Engineers can "tune" a skyscraper by moving the weight of the structure higher or lower, not unlike the way you would adjust the period of a mechanical metronome—the higher the weight, the longer the building's period. We determined the eleven-second period for the Burj Dubai based on estimates of wind vortices in the worst possible storm that is ever likely to strike the building.

As you can see, every square inch of a super-tall building is painstakingly engineered for the safety and comfort of its occupants. But these structures still possess awe-inspiring mystery, even for me—and I spend my days engineering them! I often say that skyscrapers are dreams rendered in steel and concrete. Whether they reflect the dreams of a young boy growing up in Missouri or the dreams of entire cities and nations, these structures are at the very cutting edge of current construction technologies and of our own imaginations.

Tuning the skyscraper's period is not unlike the way you adjust the period of a mechanical metronome.

## What's the Story?

1. Why do people in Dubai want to build a super-tall structure in their city?

2. What limited the height of structures in the Middle Ages?

3. What manufacturing breakthrough led to the development of taller structures in the 1800s?

## Designing with Math and Science

4. What is shear?

5. What is a truss and how does it minimize the effects of a shearing force?

6. Why is it necessary for Bill to design the Burj Dubai so that it "confuses" the wind?

7. Is concrete better at minimizing the effects of compression or tension? What is special about the concrete that Bill is using as construction material for the Burj Dubai?

8. How does the Burj Dubai reflect a New Urbanist's approach to city planning?

## What Do You Think?

9. Name a structure that is emblematic to your city, town, or region. Find out when it was built and what materials were used in its construction. What do you think would have been different if it had been built more recently?

10. What do you think superstructures of the future will be constructed of? What is special about those materials?

**13**

# *Home Sweet Home*

## Prity Rungta

*Courtesy of Prity Rungta*

**Key Concepts**
**from Previous Chapters**

2 Criteria and Constraints

4 Scale, Orthographic Drawings

11 Construction Materials

11 Foundations and Load Distribution

11 Bending, Compression, Tension

12 Trusses and Load Distribution

Constructing a building that people will live in can take months—sometimes years—of planning and execution. The task may require teams of engineers, designers, and skilled tradespeople. It involves coordinating the purchase, delivery, and use of a long list of materials and tools. And the whole process must happen within a given time frame and budget. That's why every construction project needs a manager.

My name is Prity Rungta, and I am a construction project manager for a building company in Toronto, Canada, called Bolt Developments. My company specializes in residential and commercial projects in the Toronto area. These projects can take a year or longer to complete and must be completed on time and on budget. It's my job to make sure that happens.

I got into construction when I was studying engineering in college. I took a course in construction management and loved it. Construction project managers are problem solvers. Unlike some engineers, we don't use the design process to create new technologies. Instead, we use it to determine the best possible way to complete a construction project given the key constraints of time and money.

Breaking into the construction industry was a challenge for me. I don't fit the typical mold of what most people in my position are like. People often assume that I work in this industry because I come from a family in construction and grew up around construction. That could not be further from the truth. The truth is that, aside from a course in construction management, my first exposure to the industry wasn't until my first job out of college.

I was a project coordinator of the construction of a very large house. I knew I had a lot to learn, so I asked tons of questions to the subcontractors—the plumbers, the roofers, the electricians, and many other skilled tradespeople—who were working on the project. They were always more than happy to explain their work to me. I think they appreciated the fact that I recognized their expertise even though I was part of the management team. That really helped keep communications strong. Now that I have a lot of knowledge about all aspects of building a home, I try to remember that there is something to learn from every new project.

## From Start to Finish

When my company takes on a new construction project, I first review plans with the architect. In order to communicate the design to me, the architect creates elevation and plan drawings of the structure. An **elevation view** is a scale drawing of the front view of the above-ground portion of a structure.

A **plan view** is drawn as though the ceiling and roof are removed so you can look down at how the floor is divided into rooms and different sections. The plan drawing communicates the floor plan of the structure to me.

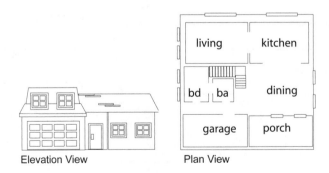

Elevation View          Plan View

*Engineering the Future: Science, Technology, and the Design Process*

The architect also usually includes a plan view of the foundation, which is the below-ground portion of the structure, as well as cross-sectional drawings, which are essentially elevation drawings of the home's interior. I can gain a lot of useful information from these drawings, including information about materials and dimensions. They are always drawn to scale, usually ¼ inch = 1 foot. Although the drawings are always to scale, all significant dimensions are marked by the architect. The scale of the drawings is used more for rough calculations.

When I understand what needs to be built, I develop a week-by-week plan for the project, detailing what will get done and when. Buildings are constructed in a series of steps, and most projects follow the steps in a similar order. However, the details of the project such as the materials, construction techniques, equipment needs, and expenses vary greatly from project to project. After I have a sense of the timeline, I begin to form a budget by pricing out materials and determining how much I'll need to pay subcontractors. When I've determined a realistic schedule and budget, I present it to my supervisors and to the clients.

## Getting Down to Work

When the plans are finalized and the budget is set, I can start ordering materials and hiring the subcontractors. After we get started, I'm on the job site every day, making sure everything gets done according to plan. This requires constant troubleshooting. Sometimes people are ill and miss work, and I have to scramble to find substitutes. Sometimes everyone is on site and ready to work, then a snowstorm hits and makes it impossible to complete the day's required tasks. Sometimes materials don't arrive on time, or equipment malfunctions. Every day, it seems, I have to design a new strategy to figure out how to make up lost time and get a house built by the deadline—all while staying within the budget.

## Laying the Foundation

The first group of contractors to arrive at the job site prepares it for construction by removing any topsoil and trees that may be in the way. This team generally brings a back-hoe or bulldozer to do the job. After the land is prepped, the team will dig a large, deep hole that is the size of the footprint of the home. A *footprint* refers to the area contained within the perimeter of the building. The foundation and part of the basement of the home will be constructed in the hole.

A *foundation* transmits loads from the structure to the ground. In most buildings, foundations extend underground. There are many different types of foundations, and when selecting the right type, architects and builders consider the size of the structure, its location, the quality of the soil on which it is being constructed, and many other variables. In all cases, a strong foundation is what anchors a structure to the ground and keeps it there. It also provides a strong base on which the above-ground part of the house will be built. A home with a weak foundation can have major structural weaknesses and even failures. So it's important that we get the foundation done right.

To form the foundation of the house we're currently working on, we constructed massive concrete footings that are 4 feet wide by 18 inches tall. These are dug into the soil around the perimeter of the hole. The basement walls are also made of poured concrete that is 22 inches thick, and they sit directly on top of the footings. These footings and foundations are about twice the size normally used on houses. When building with concrete, we first construct a wooden mold, lay reinforcing steel bars (commonly known as re-bar) inside, and then pour the liquid concrete into it. We cast the concrete in place and remove the mold, leaving the concrete part. The concrete is allowed to set for a period of days before we remove the wooden mold.

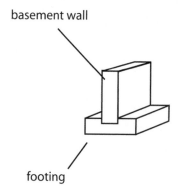
basement wall

footing

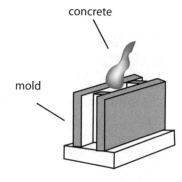
concrete

mold

# Framing the House

After the foundation and basement are complete, a crew comes to the site and begins to build the ground floor of the house on top of the basement. A floor must be very stable because its job is to support the loads in the living space above it. Remember, the dead load is the load associated with the structure itself. The live load is load not associated with the structure, such as people and furniture.

The floor is constructed of wooden joists. A *joist* is a horizontal beam, traditionally a 2-by-8-inch piece of lumber set on its edge. The joists are spaced approximately 16 inches apart, and their ends are fixed to a wooden sill plate that sits on top of the basement walls.

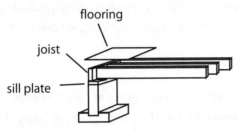

When set on its edge, a joist is more resistant to bending forces and can support higher loads than if it were laid flat. This is because when a load is placed perpendicular to the beam, the wider section of material distributes the load.

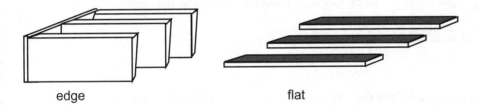

These days, it's more common to use engineered wood joists that are made of composite wood and designed to move less and provide squeak-free floors. A thin sheet of ply board goes directly on top of the joist system, and the chosen flooring material will lie on top of that. That flooring material may be hard wood, ceramic tile, slate tile, or sometimes carpeting. We won't actually put in the flooring material until we have the exterior walls of the home and the roof complete. These materials aren't designed to withstand the elements.

Every floor must be designed to support a live load. But it's not easy to predict what the live loads in a structure will be. The occupants of a house may move heavy furniture in the living room, throw dance parties for hundreds of guests, install a larger bathtub in the bathroom, or buy a small trampoline for indoor exercise. How can architects, engineers, and builders make sure that the structures they are building are strong enough to support a huge variety of live loads?

***Building codes***
are laws that specify how buildings are to be constructed. Codes regulate the structural, electrical, and plumbing systems of a building as well as fire safety design.

Building codes provide guidelines for professionals in the construction industry. They refer to these guidelines when determining how to design their structure so that it will be safe for its occupants. ***Building codes*** are community ordinances that govern how a home can be constructed or modified. Codes regulate the structural, electrical, and plumbing systems of a building as well as fire safety design.

Every community building code lists the minimum live load that a building must be designed to support. The code is usually listed as a load per unit area, which is a ***stress.*** The structural requirements dictated by the building code are different for structures with different uses, and they vary depending on the type of room.

The Massachusetts Building Code states that the minimum live load requirement for the floor of a living room in a residential building is 40 pounds for every square foot of area. The floor of a school classroom, however, must be designed to support 50 pounds per square foot.

### Massachusetts Building Code

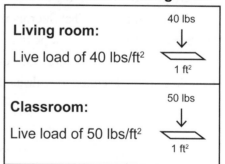

**Living room:**
Live load of 40 lbs/ft²
40 lbs
1 ft²

**Classroom:**
Live load of 50 lbs/ft²
50 lbs
1 ft²

The value in the code is calculated by estimating the highest likely live load for a particular dwelling space, then multiplying it by a safety factor. For example, the highest likely live load for a residential living room with an area the size of 400 square feet might be 4,000 pounds. This includes all furniture, people, pets, television sets, tables, and chairs, and anything else that may be in the room. Therefore, the stress, or load per unit area, that the floor of the room must be able to withstand can be calculated with the following equation:

$$\sigma = \frac{F}{A}$$

$\sigma$ = Stress
$F$ = Force of Load
$A$ = Unit Area

$$\sigma = \frac{F}{A}$$

$$\sigma = \frac{4000\ lb.}{400\ ft.^2}$$

$$\sigma = 10\frac{lb.}{ft.^2}$$

Ten pounds per square foot is quite a bit lower than the 40-pounds-per-square-foot minimum stated in the building code. That's because the building code minimum includes a safety factor. A **safety factor** is a factor by which a maximum likely stress is multiplied in order to ensure the safety of a structure. Safety factors are necessary because the occupants may use the space in unexpected ways.

$$S_F = \frac{\sigma_{designed}}{\sigma_{experienced}} \qquad S_F\,\sigma_{experienced} = \sigma_{designed}$$

$\sigma_{designed}$ = minimum stress a structure is designed to withstand

$\sigma_{experienced}$ = maximum stress a structure is likely to experience

$$S_F = \frac{\sigma_{designed}}{\sigma_{experienced}}$$

$$S_F = \frac{40\,\frac{lb.}{ft.^2}}{10\,\frac{lb}{ft.^2}}$$

$$S_F = 4$$

Before starting construction of a new structure of any kind—or renovating an older structure—architects and engineers who want to build something must present their designs and load calculations to city officials. These officials check that the structure is designed with materials and structural geometry that will meet the minimum loading requirements in the code. If a design is not up to code, it's back to the drawing board!

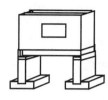

## Building the Walls

Most of the interior walls in the house I'm building now will be framed in wood. But some of the interior walls will be as high as 15 feet. In those cases, regular wood won't work for our purposes. Instead, we will use an engineered material that is made of wood strands but is much stronger. The interior wall frame will be covered with drywall, or plaster sheeting, which can be painted or finished.

The exterior walls of many houses are also constructed from wood. But in this house, our client really wanted thick and solid walls with deep window wells, so the architect designed the home with very thick concrete walls. I was happy to build the home with concrete walls but, because of our timeline, we had to construct the above-ground walls in the middle of winter. This posed a significant challenge. Concrete must be kept warm and dry in order for it to harden quickly. In Toronto, where winters can be very cold and snowy, this meant tenting the structure with tarps and using portable heaters to keep the concrete warm for weeks. This would get very expensive.

As project manager, it's my job to find the best way for the job to get done. After researching some options, we decided to use a technique for raising concrete walls using Insulated Concrete Forms (ICF). This technique involves using thick Styrofoam molds instead of wooden ones. The concrete is mixed with chemicals that heat up, and then the concrete is poured between the Styrofoam molds. The chemicals in the concrete heat the concrete as it sets, and the Styrofoam molds help keep the concrete warm much like a Styrofoam cup helps to keep hot coffee warm. Doesn't that sound like a great solution?

Using ICF to raise concrete walls

*Engineering the Future: Science, Technology, and the Design Process*

## Raising the Roof

With the walls standing, we can now put a roof on top of the house. A roof adds tremendous stability to the structure. Of course, it also protects the interior of the structure from weather.

There are many different ways to build a roof. A common way is to erect trusses underneath the roof to hold it up. The triangulated members of the truss bring extra stability. Below is a diagram of a standard roof truss.

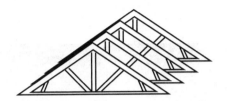 

Trusses stabilize a roof considerably, but they also limit how high the ceiling can be inside the structure. While trusses can be designed to accommodate some high ceilings, they also have some limitations. Many of our homes have very high ceilings. For this reason, we often use a "hand-cut" roof that is framed in lumber, using 2-by-8-inch boards like those in the floor. Though hand-cut roofs are more labor-intensive, they allow us to maximize our ceiling heights for dramatic effects on the interior of the home.

The truss or hand-cut roof frame is covered with layers of ply board and, finally, a roofing material. The house I'm working on now will have a slate shingle roof. Slate is a type of rock that breaks easily into thin sheets. It makes a good-looking shingle, and it's quite durable. But slate shingles are heavy—quite a bit heavier than the cedar wood or asphalt shingles that are commonly used on houses. The structural engineer had to take the high load of the slate roof into account when designing the roof and the thickness of the exterior walls of the house.

## All Systems a Go

With the walls in place and a roof over our heads, our structure is ready for the elements. But we still have *a lot* of work to do. Electricians will wire the home for electrical power. Plumbers will install the intricate systems of pipes that will bring fresh water to the home and carry wastewater away. Heating and cooling systems technicians will install climate-control systems to keep the home cozy all year round. Carpenters will construct cabinetry, build banisters in stairwells, and install flooring. Many other types of subcontractors will leave their mark before the home is move-in ready.

So, as you can see, building a house requires a tremendous amount of planning and teamwork, as well as ongoing troubleshooting. It also requires keeping up with new technologies like the Insulated Concrete Forms that help us do our jobs better. My favorite part of the construction process comes at the very end, when I take a step back and look at the beautiful home we just made. It's a feeling of accomplishment like no other. More often than not, we've built someone's dream home—and we did it on time and on budget.

Your apartment normally experiences around 5,000 pounds of force from live loads. If the building is required by law to have a safety factor of 4, how much stress must it be able to withstand? The building is 500 square feet.

## ① Define the Problem

What is the problem asking for?

The problem is asking for the maximum amount of stress the building should be designed to withstand.

We have learned that this type of stress is a particular type of stress value, called $\sigma_{designed}$.

So, the problem wants you to find $\sigma_{designed}$.

## ② Research the Problem

What information do you have?
What information do you need?

You are given values for the live load the building experiences, the square footage of the building, and the safety factor ($S_F$).

$S_F = 4$
$A = 500$ ft.²
$F = 5,000$ lb.

## ③ Develop Solutions and Select the Best Solution

Which equations do you use?
What do you solve for?

It's not always easy to know what formulas you should use, and you can often use different formulas to solve for the same thing, but as you get more familiar with your areas of study, it will get easier!

Looking at the list of values you have, you can say useful formulas would be formulas dealing with safety factor and stress.

$$1 \quad S_F = \frac{\sigma_{designed}}{\sigma_{experienced}} \qquad 2 \quad \sigma = \frac{F}{A}$$

## ④ Solve the Problem

Because, you want to find $\sigma_{designed}$, you can rearrange the first equation to be

$$3 \quad \sigma_{designed} = S_F \left( \sigma_{experienced} \right)$$

$$\sigma_{designed} = 4 \left( \sigma_{experienced} \right)$$

You don't have the value for $\sigma_{experienced}$, but with the information you have, you can use

$$2 \quad \sigma_{experienced} = \frac{F}{A}$$

$$\sigma_{experienced} = \frac{5000 \; lb.}{500 \; ft.^2}$$

$$\sigma_{experienced} = 10 \frac{lb.}{ft.^2}$$

Now you have all the values you need. Going back to equation 3,

$$\sigma_{designed} = 4 \left( \sigma_{experienced} \right)$$
$$\sigma_{designed} = 4 \left( 10 \frac{lb.}{ft.^2} \right)$$
$$\sigma_{designed} = 40 \frac{lb.}{ft.^2}$$

## ⑤ Test and Evaluate

What does it all mean?

Does it make sense that $\sigma_{designed} = 40$ lb./ft.²?

Well, if $\sigma_{experienced}$ is 10 lb./ft.² and $\sigma_{designed}$ is 40 lb./ft.², that means the building typically experiences 10 pounds of load per square feet, but it can withstand 40 pounds of load per square foot. So the safety factor is 4, meaning the designed stress is 4 times the amount of stress that is typically experienced. That makes a building pretty safe.

## What's the Story?

1. Prity does not design structures, but she says she does use the engineering design process. How?

2. What is the primary way that the architect communicates his or her building plans to Prity's team?

3. Prity describes two new construction technologies that help her team deliver a higher-quality product for the money. What are they?

## Designing with Math and Science

4. You are an structural engineer working for a design firm, and you have been given the task of designing a scaffold that can support a load of 300 pounds. The scaffold must have a safety factor of 2. How many pounds must your design be able to support?

## Connecting the Dots

5. Sketch a plan view and elevation view of your school's lunchroom or library. The drawings should not include furnishings, but they should include architectural features such as windows, doors, pillars, or skylights.

## What Do You Think?

6. Prity explains that she learned a lot about the construction industry by asking questions of the people she was working with. Describe a time when you've had to ask a lot of questions to learn what you needed to know in order to do a job or an assignment well.

# 14

## *From the Ground Up*

### Cathy Bazán-Arias

---

⚙ **Key Concepts**
**from Previous Chapters**

- **2** Redesign
- **11** Loads
- **11** Foundation
- **11** Construction Materials—Characteristics
- **13** Stress

---

The Leaning Tower of Pisa is a famous example of what can go wrong when engineers and architects don't know what they are building on. Even during its construction, which began in 1173, the Tower began to lean to one side. We now know that the Tower leaned because the soil beneath it, which contained a lot of sand, could not bear the load of the structure. Engineers have kept the Tower standing through the centuries by continuously repairing it, restabilizing it, and even altering the soil.

It's a lot more cost-effective to make sure the soil underneath can support the structure's load long before construction starts. As a geotechnical engineer, that's a big part of my job. My name is Cathy Bazán-Arias, and I'm a senior engineer at GAI Consultants, Inc., an engineering firm based in Pittsburgh, Pennsylvania.

My company provides engineering expertise on a wide range of projects, from designing and building dams to upgrading electric transmission lines to improving mass-transit systems. Our clients include private companies, government agencies, and even international organizations.

As a little girl growing up in Mexico, I knew that I wanted to become an engineer. My father was a professor of engineering at a major university in Mexico City. Though engineering was not considered a profession for women, my father would take me to work with him. He always found ways to involve me in his engineering projects. We moved to the United States when I was starting eighth grade. There I found more opportunities to get involved with student engineering and science programs. And I met more female engineers who I took as role models. I studied civil engineering at the University of Pittsburgh for my undergraduate degree. Then I went on to get a master's degree and a Ph.D. in geotechnical engineering there as well.

## A Matter of Matter

The prefix "geo" is a Greek word that means Earth or land. So it makes sense that geotechnical engineers specialize in designing how structures or underground parts of structures interact with the land they are standing on. To do my job, I need to know all about a structure's geometry, materials, and loads. As you can see, geotechnical engineering is closely related to structural engineering. I have training in both disciplines, and that dual training often comes in handy.

One project I'm working on illustrates how my dual training helps. My team recently took on a project improving an electric power transmission line. Transmission lines carry electrical current from a power station—where the electricity is generated—over long distances to the communities that will use the electricity. The towers that hold up the electrical lines are spaced about every 300–500 yards for hundreds of miles, and must be designed to stand on a wide range of terrains—including forests, agricultural lands, and rocky foothills.

In this photo of a transmission tower under construction, you can see the above-ground structure of the tower quite well. But what keeps it standing? The visible part of the tower would not be stable without a foundation. If there is too much movement of the tower base due to poor foundation performance, there could be an above-ground structural failure and wire breakage. If wires break, the whole power line will stop working.

*Courtesy of GAI Consultants, Inc.*

In the Northeastern United States, it is often necessary to upgrade transmission lines. Typically, this requires constructing some new towers and renovating some older ones. In either case, we must make sure that the towers' components—above-ground and below-ground—are constructed with strong enough materials. We must also verify that the towers are on soils that will support them without excessive movement. This means understanding how the soils and the structure will interact.

## Tower Design Criteria

Electric power transmission lines have been around for a long time. We don't need to reinvent the wheel, but we do want to improve upon older designs. Transmissions structures are typically made from steel, wood, and concrete. And they are usually tall and narrow. The same is true for the new towers we are designing. They will be 90–100 feet tall on average. The taller the towers, the fewer towers that are needed over any given distance. This is because the current carrying wires will be strung from tower to tower.

There will be some slack in the wires, and the wires will hang lowest at the farthest point between the two towers. If the towers are too short and spaced too far apart, the current carrying wire will hang dangerously close to the ground, tree tops, or other human activity. But if the towers are very tall, we can space them farther apart and still not leave the sagging wire near people, because it is still high. At the same time, we want the towers themselves to be as narrow as possible. A narrow tower requires less space on the ground. This is advantageous because the towers may go through populated areas where land prices are high. Narrow, sleek towers will also be less obtrusive on the landscape than bulky towers. The towers' neighbors will appreciate that!

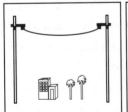 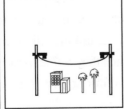 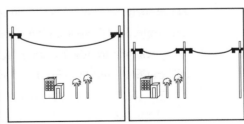

Taller transmission towers can have greater distances between them.

In this case, three short towers are needed to cover the same distance that two tall towers cover.

Even though the towers will be tall and narrow, they must be quite strong. They will have to remain standing during high winds. And in the Northern United States, the line may get loaded with snow and ice in the winter. Ice loading is a big concern. Ice can get very thick and add considerable weight to the line. Ice loading has torn down towers in the past, leading to major electrical outages that affected millions of people. We want to do everything we can to avoid a major outage on our lines.

The foundation for each tower varies, but a typical foundation looks something like the diagram below. The structure's vertical poles rest on cylindrical foundations, which are embedded in the ground at a depth between 15 and 20 percent of the height of the pole. So a 50-foot pole will have a foundation 10 feet underground.

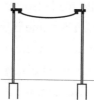

The most common material for transmission-line foundations is reinforced concrete. Steel may be used if the soils in the area will not bear the weight of concrete. Steel is also used for the foundations in areas where it is hard to get the required materials into the construction area by truck. In this case, the foundation components have to be flown by helicopter. The geometry of the foundations may change depending on how the tower's load needs to be distributed, so that the soil can support it.

## Selecting Materials

A large part of the job involves selecting the right materials for the foundation and the above-ground portion of the towers. We know that the materials we will use to build the towers are most likely going to be steel, concrete, and wood. These materials have been used to build electric power transmission lines for a long time. But there are many, many types of each material. We want to choose the types that are ideally suited for the unique climates and terrains that our line will traverse, and the variety of loads they will experience.

To select the very best material for our purposes, we need to compare how different materials behave under stress. The stresses could be a result of compression, tension, torsion, or shearing forces. For a long time, engineers have studied how commonly used materials behave under such stresses and documented the results.

That means that we don't have to test commonly used materials ourselves. We usually look up a material in a reference manual to learn how it behaves under different types of stresses in different conditions. If we are using a new material, or are using a material in a new and untested way, we must test those materials ourselves.

*Engineering the Future: Science, Technology, and the Design Process*

In addition to comparing how materials behave, my team will also compare performance and cost. Performance means how long the material will do its job well. The towers will experience a lot of wear and tear due to seasonal temperature fluctuations, snow, rain, and sun, and even the chemistry of the soil in which they are embedded. Materials respond differently to these stressors. Wood breaks down over time, and steel can corrode. We know that the towers will need regular maintenance to stay in working order. But if they need frequent maintenance, in addition to the normal care, those costs could add up.

The selection of the right material also requires us to determine how long we want the structure to last, and how much money we can spend. Many high-performance materials come with a high price. And we often don't need a high-performance material to do the job well. If we determine we only need a tower to stand for ten years, a lower-grade steel may serve our purposes just as well as a more expensive high-grade steel. However, a higher-performance material may save money over time because it will require less maintenance. Based on the performance criteria, we can determine the most economical material that will still get the job done well.

Every material changes shape, or deforms, in response to stress. It's easy to visualize this deformation in a rubber band. When you pull on both ends of a rubber band, you apply stress to the material. In response, the rubber band increases in length. **Strain** is a measure of how much a material deforms as compared with its original size. Strain can be calculated using the following equation:

$$Strain\ (\varepsilon) = \frac{\Delta L}{L}$$

Original Length

Change in length

$\Delta L$ = **Change in length** of a material after stress is applied

$L$ = **Original length** of the material

When selecting materials, Dr. Bazán-Arias must compare the strength of materials. **Strength** is a calculation of how much stress a material can support without deforming in a way that compromises the integrity of the material. As you recall, stress is the load or force per unit area of material. Stress is calculated with the following equation:

$$Stress\ (\sigma) = \frac{F}{A}$$

$F = Load$
$A = Cross\text{-}sectional\ area$

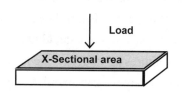

When engineers test materials, they often subject a sample of the material to different stresses and plot how much a material strains on a graph. These graphs, like the one shown on the right, are called stress-strain curves. Engineers can get a lot of useful information about how a material behaves by looking at a stress-strain curve.

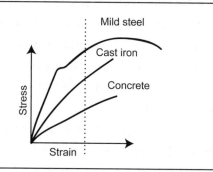

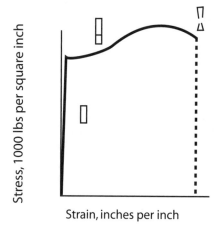

Stress, 1000 lbs per square inch

Strain, inches per inch

**Point 1 to Point 2 *elastic deformation*:** As you can see, this part of the graph is very straight and steep. This means that as stress increases, strain increases very slowly. In other words, the material does not deform very much, and when the stress is removed, the material returns to its original shape. This is called elastic deformation.

**Point 2 is the *elastic limit*:** After this point, the material does not return to its original shape.

**Point 2 to Point 3 *plastic deformation*:** When stress reaches the level indicated at point 2, called the elastic limit, the material begins to behave very differently. Strain increases very quickly with even small increases in stress. For example, when a piece of metal reaches this point, it starts to stretch like taffy. Furthermore, the deformation is permanent. Once the stress passes the elastic limit, the material will not return to its original form.

**Point 3 is the *failure point*:** The material breaks, so it is no longer possible to increase the level of stress.

# Bringing It Back Down to Earth

To make our material selections, we must know what types of soils we'll be building on. Depending on the type of terrain we find, we may need to alter the design of the foundation, and possibly the tower as well.

To learn about the different types of terrains that we may encounter while building our towers, my team hires scientists who have spent years studying the soils in the area. Because the transmission line project covers such a wide range of terrains, it would require a lot more work, and time, for my team to learn everything we need to know about the land in the region by doing our own research. It's much more cost effective to hire a consultant who has already done the research.

The underground structure of the towers will extend into the substrata, an underground layer of Earth. The substrata may contain rock, gravel, sand, clay, silt, decomposing plant matter, or any combination of these. Each type of soil behaves differently under stress, and the same soil types may behave differently in different conditions.

Two soil types we commonly encounter are sand and clay. Sand is very strong when it's wet. When the sand is dry, though, it can't hold much weight at all. If you've ever walked on a sandy beach or stepped into a child's sand box, then you've experienced how sand gives way under your weight. Clay soils, on the other hand, can be very strong, but if the load of a structure is not distributed well over the clay, it may compress the clay. If the clay is compressed, part or all of the structure could sink.

The behavior of the soils in response to different stresses has also been studied and documented. The properties of different soil types and how they respond to different stresses can be described by stress-strain curves. These curves are critical to determine how a soil may behave when subjected to different types of loads.

As soon as my team has information about the terrain and understands the soil and its load limitations, we can start to make decisions about how to design the foundation in terms of materials and structural geometry. Sometimes we learn that we need to site a tower in a different location because the soil won't bear the load of the tower, regardless of how well we design it! If we can't change the location of the tower, we may attempt to dig out some of the problematic substrata and replace it with stronger material.

When it comes to structures, what you see is not all you get. An underground system, which includes both naturally occurring and human-made materials, is necessary to keep a structure standing. As a geotechnical engineer, I've had the pleasure of applying my academic knowledge to the task of building structures from the ground up.

## Terms of Failure Analysis

pre   at   post
σ     σ    σ

Elastic Band

### Elastic Deformation:
Material returns to its original shape after stress is applied.

### Elastic Limit:
Point where elastic deformation ends and plastic deformation begins.

pre   at   post
σ     σ    σ

Weight

### Plastic Deformation:
Material does not return to its original shape after stress is applied.

### Failure Point:
Point where the material breaks or fractures.

pre   at   post
σ     σ    σ

Weight

*Engineering the Future: Science, Technology, and the Design Process*

## What's the Story?

1.  Dr. Bazán-Arias is a geotechnical engineer by training, but she also has some expertise in structural engineering. Why does she believe having both is helpful?

2.  What are the major factors that engineers consider when selecting materials for a job?

3.  What kinds of information can engineers get by looking at stress-strain curves?

## Designing with Math and Science

4.  Look at the stress-strain curve below. How much does the material strain under 25 PSI of stress? Will the material return to its original shape after a stress of this magnitude has been applied?

5.  What is the elastic limit of the material, and how can you tell? How will the material behave under loads higher than the elastic limit?

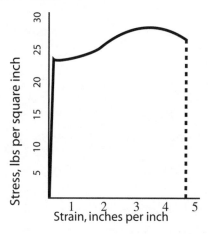

## Connecting the Dots

6.  Foundations are important parts of the structural designs described in the three previous chapters. Write a one-sentence description of each of the following structures' foundations: 1. The Leonard P Zakim Bridge; 2. The Burj Dubai; 3. A house; 4. A transmission tower.

## What Do You Think?

7.  Dr. Bazán-Arias also designs landfills for GAI Consulting. Do some research in the library or on the Internet and write two paragraphs about landfill design. In your response, explain some of the decisions that engineers designing a landfill may have to make in terms of location, material selection, and structural geometry.

# 15

## *Building Green*

### Chris Benedict

---

**Key Concepts**
**from Previous Chapters**

**7** Systems

**11** Loads

**11** Construction Materials—Characteristics

---

Winters get very cold in New York City. But, obviously, that doesn't keep people from living here. Technology allows people to live in some pretty extreme climates. Our structures protect us from the harsh conditions. We've developed climate-control systems for our structures that keep us warm in the winter and cool in the summer. The problem is that many climate-control systems require a lot of energy.

I'm Chris Benedict. I design buildings that are energy efficient, which means that I focus on ways to design buildings that use less energy to keep their occupants comfortable. Architects like me have been nicknamed "green" architects because we design buildings that have fewer negative impacts on the environment.

Being an architect takes a lot of study, preparation, and hard work. I studied architecture at The Cooper Union for the Advancement of Science and Art, a private college in New York City that specializes in art, architecture, and engineering. Like most new architects, I worked in several different architecture offices after I graduated. When I started my own architecture business, I knew that I wanted to introduce green concepts into every new design. Green buildings, when designed well, come alive because they respond to their environment. I love how elegant and creative green design can be.

Even though I'm no longer in school or an apprentice, my learning hasn't stopped. Far from it! I'm always attending conferences, reading about energy-efficient design, and learning from my previous experiences. I'm also always trying to spread the word to others in the building industry and the general public about the importance of green architecture. I do this by sharing my experiences and giving tours of building sites. That's one reason why I'm happy to have the opportunity to describe my work to you.

## What Is Energy?

In my line of work, people talk a lot about saving or conserving energy, but just what do we mean by "energy"? Even though it's a term you've probably heard and used many times, it's not so easy to get a handle on what it is. We all have direct experience with energy. We feel like we have more energy after eating a chocolate bar or drinking a glass of orange juice. We're "out of energy" at the end of a long day. We know that we need energy to run our electronic devices. Energy is also needed to move things such as cars, bicycles, or paddle wheels. And energy is necessary to raise the temperature of bathwater or to heat up a home.

What's tricky about energy is that it's not a substance. You can't pick up a handful of energy. But energy acts like a substance in many ways. Like matter, energy cannot be created or destroyed. I know it seems like matter can be destroyed. If you burn a piece of paper, it seems to disappear, right? But the matter that made up the paper is not gone. The paper has been converted to ashes and smoke. If you were to burn the piece of paper in a jar that trapped all of the smoke and ash and then use a scale to find the mass of the substance in the jar, you'd find that it has the exact same mass as the piece of paper.

Burn

Mass = Mass

*Engineering the Future: Science, Technology, and the Design Process*

Physicists refer to this as the ***Law of Conservation of Mass.*** The law basically states that the mass of the inputs to a system will always be the same as the mass of the outputs from a system, regardless of the processes involved. So if you ripped the paper into little shreds instead of burning it, you would still have the same amount of matter.

The same is true for energy. The energy inputs of a system will always equal the energy outputs, regardless of the processes. This is referred to as the ***Law of Conservation of Energy.*** While energy cannot be created or destroyed, it can be stored or transferred from place to place. A fuel such as wood, gasoline, or oil stores energy. When these fuels are burned, they transfer their stored energy to the objects in their environment.

As a green architect, I'm interested in finding the best ways to heat homes and keep them warm. In a standard home heating system, a machine called a ***boiler*** burns natural gas or oil. Most of the energy released from the burning fuel is transferred to a drum of water inside the boiler. The hot fluid is then pumped to radiators in the rooms of the building. The radiators then get hot and transfer energy to the air in the room. After water in the radiators transfer its energy to the air in the room, it flows back into the boiler to be heated again.

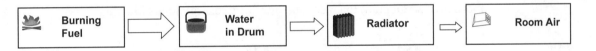

| 🔥 Burning Fuel | ⟹ | 🪣 Water in Drum | ⟹ | ▦ Radiator | ⟹ | Room Air |

In order to keep track of how energy moves through a system, it's useful for engineers to identify the different objects in the system. In the above example, one might define the system as consisting of four objects: the fuel, the water in the drum, the radiator, and the room air. The arrows indicate energy transfer from one object to the next within the system.

The purpose of the system is to heat up the air in the room. It makes sense to consider the room air as an object outside of the heating system. The darker lines in the diagram on the next page indicate system boundaries. How we define the systems is really up to us—it's arbitrary. Engineers define systems in ways that help them keep track of how the energy moves through and beyond the system.

In this diagram, energy crosses a system boundary when it is transferred from the radiator to the room air. When energy crosses a system boundary and causes the objects outside of the system boundary to get hot, we call this **heating.** The energy transferred is called *thermal energy.*

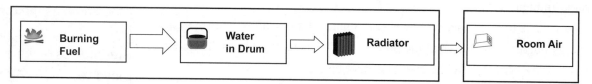

In our daily language, we often talk about "heat" as if it is an object. We might say to a friend, "This radiator is giving off a lot of heat." Scientists and engineers think of heat a little differently. To us, heat is not an object. Rather, it's a process by which energy is transferred across a boundary. The room air is not the only object outside of the heating system that is getting hotter. The air around the boiler, the pipes, the air around the pipes, and many other objects also may get hotter. If you stood close to the boiler, you would get hotter too. The goal of the heating system is to transfer energy to the room air, but some of the energy is heating other objects. Engineers often refer to this energy as "lost." Of course, it's not lost. We know where it is. It's just not in a place that is useful to us. A more precise diagram that accounts for "lost" energy looks like this:

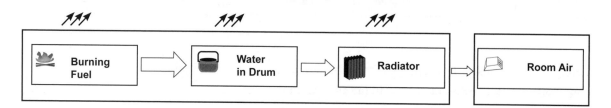

A major engineering challenge is to reduce these losses, so that the room is heated at maximum efficiency. To meet this challenge, engineers need to understand the relationship between thermal energy and temperature.

## What Is Temperature?

You can see that temperature has something to do with energy. You know that temperature is a measure of "hotness" and "coldness," and that the room air gets hotter when energy is transferred to it. What is different about a "hot" room or a "cold" room is the concentration of energy in the room. *Temperature* can be defined as the concentration of thermal energy in a substance. Temperature changes are one type of evidence that energy transfer is taking place as thermal energy is moving from an area of high concentration to low concentration.

## So, What's the Problem?

The heating systems in use today are very effective in keeping our homes, offices, and other building comfortably warm, even on the coldest winter day. But the technologies used in most heating systems rely heavily on fossil fuels—oil, gas, and coal—which contribute to a number of health and environmental problems. Burning these fuels releases pollutants such as carbon monoxide and nitrous oxide into the air, and they are unhealthy to breathe. Many scientists believe these gases also contribute to global climate change. Extracting and transporting fossil fuels poses other serious problems. Because oil, natural, gas, and coal are found deep under the Earth's surface, people must build complex systems of wells, mines, pipelines, and roadways to extract them. This has led to habitat loss and degradation in some beautiful natural places on our planet. And heating homes with fossil fuels can be expensive. In some parts of the United States, many families simply cannot afford to keep their homes warm in the winter.

Given all of the problems associated with burning fossil fuels, I feel that we must find ways to use less of them. One way to reduce consumption is to construct buildings with heating systems that require us to burn as little fuel as possible while keeping us comfortably sheltered from the elements.

## Keeping Warm while Conserving Energy

Right now, I'm overseeing the construction of several six-story low-income-housing buildings that I designed. When they are done, these buildings will be rented to people, often families, who don't have a lot of money. The rents will stay fixed for a long time, so that the tenants can afford to keep living in them even as housing prices climb year after year. Surprisingly, we are designing a "green" building for the same amount of money that a conventional building costs. In fact, this green building will save money in the long run because the owners and tenants won't spend as much money on heating.

I asked my colleague Henry Gifford to design a more efficient heating system for the building. Henry is a heating systems specialist, an essential team member in the effort to build an energy-efficient building. I met Henry at a green design conference a few years ago, and since then we have collaborated on a number of projects together. He has developed a heating system for the low-income-housing project that includes a thermostat in every room. A *thermostat* can measure the temperature of air and turn on the heating system automatically if the temperature drops below a certain temperature. It turns the heating system switch off as soon as the air is warm enough.

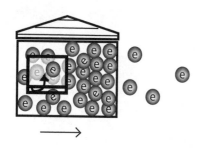

A lot of apartments have thermostats, but few have thermostats in every room. Why are more thermostats better? Well, let's say it's mid-January. An apartment has three very warm rooms and one cold room. Unfortunately, the only thermostat in the apartment is located in the cold room. The thermostat keeps the heating system on, making the hot rooms even hotter. When the tenant gets home from work at the end of every day, she has to open windows in the hot rooms in order to make those rooms more comfortable. Think of all that energy going out the window! If every room has its own thermostat, we don't have this problem. In fact, Henry estimates that the additional thermostats reduce the amount of hot water that the boiler has to produce by about 25 percent. This allows us to install a smaller boiler, which saves cost.

## The Great Escape

With Henry on my team, I knew we'd find an efficient way to heat the building. But I also knew I needed to find a good way to keep the energy inside the building once it was there. Warm air escapes buildings through even the tiniest openings around doors or windows and at the seals of vents. Thermal energy even passes through walls!

Why does it do this? That's something fundamental to the nature of energy: When there is a difference in temperature in two objects, thermal energy will transfer from the hotter to the cooler object. The transfer will continue until there is no temperature difference.

You can see this is true in the case of the boiler in the heating system. When the boiler is first turned on, the burning fuel is much hotter than the water in the boiler. The burning fuel transfers energy to the water. The hot water is then pumped to the cool radiators, which get hot. Now, of course the radiators are hotter than the room air. So what happens? The radiators transfer energy to the room air. The transfer continues until the room air is the same temperature as the radiators.

But as soon as the home is heated, the interior of the building has a higher temperature than the air outside. Consequently, thermal energy naturally transfers to the air outside of the home, even through the walls!

> Energy will always transfer from the hotter to the cooler object. The transfer will continue until the difference disappears.

One way to keep the energy inside a warm home from escaping is to make sure that the windows and doors are airtight when they are closed, because warm air can escape. To ensure this, we use a blower-door during construction to test for air tightness. A blower-door is a fan with fabric around it. The fabric attaches to the doorway. If any air is moving through the doorway when the door is closed, the fan blades will turn. Based on how much the fan blades turn, we can measure the amount of air escaping through the doorway and determine the best way to make the door more airtight.

To keep energy from moving through the walls, we put insulation in the walls. A thermal *insulator* is a material through which energy does not flow well. An insulator is the opposite of a *conductor,* through which energy passes easily.

To describe how effective a material is as an insulator, we give it an "R-value." The R stands for "resistance," and it characterizes the material's ability to resist the flow of energy. A larger R-value means greater resistance. Therefore, a material with a higher R-value is a better insulator. Below is a chart with R-values for some common materials. We use mineral wool insulation because it has a high R-value and does not burn easily.

An *insulator* is a material through which energy does not flow well.

A *conductor* is a material through which energy flows well.

| Material | R-value |
|---|---|
| Wood | 0.91 |
| Fiberboard | 2.78 |
| Fiberglass | 3.90 |
| Styrofoam | 3.57 |
| Cellulose Insulation | 3.5 |
| Mineral Wool | 3.0 |

The outer walls of the building have three layers: brick on the outside, followed by a layer of mineral wool insulation, and concrete block on the inside. To test how well these walls resist the flow of energy, we take photographs of our building with infrared cameras. The infrared camera images show us where energy was escaping from some of the walls in the building. So we add more insulation in those areas.

Unlike a typical home that uses plaster or sheetrock on the inside walls, I used concrete block, which acts as a thermal mass. In engineering, the word "thermal" is used to describe systems that transfer energy to raise or lower the temperatures of objects inside or outside of the system. A *thermal mass* is a component of a building where materials absorb and store energy. Concrete is often used as a thermal mass because it easily absorbs and stores energy. It is also very slow to change temperature. During winter, the building's heating system transfers energy to the concrete. The mass of the concrete stores the energy and slowly releases it into the apartments. In the summer, the bricks and the insulation protect the concrete from being heated by the summer sun. Instead, the concrete absorbs the energy from the interior of the building, cooling it down.

## Carrying the Load

Besides adding thermal stability, the concrete layers also provide critical structural support for each floor. The floors of the building are made of concrete planks, which are essentially a set of concrete blocks connected with steel rods running through them. Concrete alone cannot bear the necessary loads that the floor will experience. That's why the concrete planks are reinforced with steel rods. A floor experiences compression on the upper side and tension on the bottom side. Concrete is very good at withstanding compression forces. That's why it's often used in columns or pillars, which must withstand compression. But concrete does not withstand tension very well. Steel holds up well under both tension and compression. So the two materials work together as a team: The concrete withstands the compression and the steel reinforcing rods run through the concrete withstand the tension.

## Green Architecture Is a Team Effort

My good working relationship with Henry is but one example of the importance of teamwork. For the low-income-housing project, I've worked more closely with engineers and contractors than an architect usually does. Typically, an architect will design a building. This includes the layouts, the colors, the way the building looks, the detailing. She will then hand the plans over to structural engineers. The engineers do the calculations necessary to size the structural beams, heating units, insulation, ventilation fans, water pipes, and more. The architect's plans and the engineers' calculations are given to a contractor, who organizes all of the skilled technicians—the carpenters, plumbers, roofers, bricklayers, and others—who construct the building and all of its systems.

Cross-section of the outer wall of the building

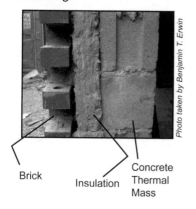

*Photo taken by Benjamin T. Erwin*

Brick  Insulation  Concrete Thermal Mass

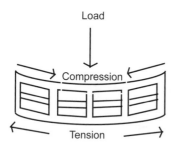

Steel beams support the portion of the plank under tension. Steel withstands tension well.

*Engineering the Future: Science, Technology, and the Design Process*

Now that I am a green architect, I see a building as a system made up of interdependent subsystems. The structural elements, the support beams and walls, the heating systems, the electrical systems, the water systems, and the other parts of a building influence each other and must work together. For this reason, the people involved in constructing the building must work closely together as well.

There is another important player when it comes to constructing a building: the building inspector. A **building inspector** is a government employee who knows the country, state, and city building code laws, and makes sure that every architect follows them. The building inspector also makes sure that buildings meet health, safety, and energy codes. These codes cover such things as where smoke detectors must be placed, the width of doorways, and the loads the building must withstand. When an architect first comes up with a set of plans, the owner of the building or the contractor will take the plans to the building inspector for approval. After the building inspector approves the plans, the building permit is granted.

Putting a steel-reinforced concrete plank in place

## The Total Package

Every aspect of my building must be designed with sustainability in mind. Behind one of the six-story buildings I am working on, we are designing a landscaped backyard area for residents to enjoy. The pavement will be slanted so that rainwater will run off of it into underground pits of sand called **recharge beds.** These beds store the rainwater then slowly release it back to the plants over time. This conserves water because, even on dry days, the garden won't need to be watered from the municipal water supply. It will receive plenty of water from the recharge beds. On another building down the street, we are putting in a community garden on the roof. Roof gardens are not only great places to hang out, but they also hold rain water on the roof during strong rainstorms and keep our sewage treatment plants from being overwhelmed with waste water. In New York City, if the sewage treatment plant is overwhelmed, it releases untreated sewage into the rivers.

As you are starting to see, I am involved in every detail of the buildings that I design, and all of the details are critical to the function of the building as a whole. One more problem that I have to contend with in a big city is pigeons. To prevent pigeons from hanging out and nesting above the windows, I designed the concrete ledges to be narrow enough so that the pigeons won't land. I have a bet with Henry as to whether my design will keep pigeons away. Henry thinks they won't work. He says he's seen pigeons cling to razor-thin ledges. Well, we'll see who wins the bet!

 ## What's the Story?

1. What problem do green architects try to solve?

2. What makes the heating system in Chris's green building more efficient than the heating system in "conventional" buildings?

3. Make a list of four materials that Chris will use in her building and briefly explain the function of each material.

## Designing with Math and Science

4. Draw an energy diagram of a toaster heating up a slice of bread.

5. What's the difference between an insulator and a conductor? Would an engineer choose a good insulator or a good conductor as a material for a coffee mug? What about a saucepan?

6. Which is a better insulator, wood or cellulose insulation? (Use the R-value chart earlier in the chapter.) How do you know?

 ## Connecting the Dots

7. Many of the engineers in this book discuss the importance of teamwork. Why is teamwork so critical when it comes to designing green buildings? How is this different from the teamwork in "The Making of a New Balance Shoe" and other earlier chapters?

## What Do You Think?

8. Look around your school building and list at least three ways the building could be designed to better conserve energy.

9. Chris talks about the role of a building inspector. Why is this an important role? What might result if cities and towns did not employ building inspectors?

# 16

## A Race for the Sun

### Lauren Stencel

Photo taken by Donald Foster

Copyright © 2008 Museum of Science, Boston

### Key Concepts
#### from Previous Chapters

7 Systems

15 Differences Drive Change

15 Energy Transfer and Storage

15 Heating

15 Temperature

15 Insulator

Every few years, college teams from around the world meet at the National Mall, which stretches from the White House to the National Monument in Washington, D.C., to compete in a 21-day decathlon. But this is not a usual decathlon. In the National Solar Decathlon, each team builds a home that must function independently—not connected to electricity, water, or waste lines—for eleven whole days.

My name is Lauren Stencel, and I am a solar decathlete. My team is from the University of Massachusetts, Dartmouth, where I study chemistry. Last year, I read about an opportunity to join the school's solar decathlon team and I couldn't pass it up. I've always cared about the environment. When I was growing up, my mom was a big environmentalist and taught me about the importance of recycling and conservation.

Our team plans to donate our home to Habitat for Humanity, an organization that provides homes at much-reduced prices to people who need them.

This project is a lot of work. We're raising all of the money to pay for the costs of building the home ourselves—about $95,000. And, of course, we're doing most of the design and construction as well. The team members take classes in energy-efficient technology and architecture, but we also devote plenty of time to building the house. We're constructing a small-scale test home on campus. In my first day building the house, I hit my thumb with a hammer, got a massive splinter in my arm, and I went home with blisters on both hands. But I don't mind the hard work or the splinters. I believe that what we're doing is important. Not only are we providing a home for someone who needs it, but we're also learning about technologies that can help solve some of the serious problems we face today. When I was in high school, I never imagined that, as a college student, I could work on projects that had such a positive impact.

As we design our home, we have two different sets of criteria: Not only does our house have to function on the National Mall, it also must eventually function as a family's home. For this reason, we are planning to build the house on my college campus. Then we'll move the house to the competition site on a big flatbed truck. After the competition is over, we'll take the home to its permanent location in a Washington, D.C., neighborhood and get it ready for the family to move in.

## The Comfort Zone

All systems of a house are important, but a reliable climate-control system is absolutely critical for getting through a cold winter or a hot summer. The primary function of a house, after all, is to shelter inhabitants from the elements. In Washington, D.C., the winters can be well below freezing, and the summers run hot and humid.

Fortunately, there are many ways to design a house to take advantage of the sun for heating and cooling. Ideally, an architect should put large windows on the home, positioned to face due south. That way the sun can shine through the windows and warm up the air inside the house. Of course, if the home is located in the southern hemisphere, the windows must be oriented to face north to collect the most sunlight.

The sun can also warm the thermal mass of the home—concrete or flagstone floors or walls. Then, at night when it's chilly, the floors or walls will release stored energy to the home, providing warmth. This is called *passive solar heating.*

In the summer, the windows have overhangs so that they block the midday sunlight, when the sun is highest in the sky. This solar shielding helps to keep the air inside the home comfortably cool. The house also relies on good insulation to keep hot air out. Remember that an insulator is a material that resists the flow of energy. When it's warm outdoors, the insulation keeps energy outside the home from creeping in.

We're building our home out of a very effective insulator. It's basically a thick slab of polystyrene—the material used in disposable coffee cups—sandwiched between two pieces of ply board. A company in Michigan makes the boards in 24 × 8–foot panels. We're having the panels cut to meet the dimensions of the house. The panels will hold up the ceiling of the one-story home. We're using the panels to make the walls, the ceilings, and the floors. Polystyrene has a very high R-value, which is a measure of how well a material resists the flow of energy, so it will keep the energy outside of the home in the summer and inside in the winter.

Our home will face due south in its permanent location. It will include large windows on the front of the home to collect the most sunlight. But we're installing another heating system that will work regardless of how the house is positioned. This *active solar heating* system uses pumps to circulate a "working fluid"—usually water or antifreeze—through collectors and into storage tanks. The collectors, which are located on the roof, use energy from the sun to warm up the fluid, and the storage tanks hold the fluid until it is used to warm up the home.

A common type of solar collector is a flat, rectangular box that is about one meter by two meters long with a dark surface that absorbs energy from the sunlight and becomes very hot. The energy is transferred to pipes that coil through the collector. The pipes then transfer energy to a fluid flowing through them. The hot fluid flows to a highly insulated tank, which stores the hot fluid until it is used to heat the home. Insulation prevents the heat from escaping from the collector.

> **Passive solar heating** refers to designing a home to take advantage of sunlight for heating.

In a passive solar heating system, sunlight shines through large south-facing windows onto a concrete or ceramic floor, heating it up.

> **Active solar heating** systems use pumps to circulate a fluid that has been heated by the sun.

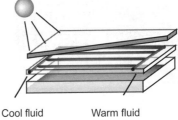

Cool fluid enters          Warm fluid exits

The collector has a clear window over the top, which allows the sun's rays to reach the collector but prevents the wind from cooling it. The plate and pipes in the collector are usually made of copper because copper has high thermal conductivity, which means that it transmits energy well.

After we have all this hot water in the storage tanks, we need to transfer the energy it contains into the living space of our home. Most homes have radiators through which hot water from the furnace circulates. The radiators become hot and, in turn, they transfer energy to the room air, heating up the room.

We could use this approach, and some solar homes do, but in our house, we're planning to embed radiator pipes in the floor. The pipes will weave back and forth in order to cover the entire floor, just under the surface. When hot water circulates through these pipes, energy is transferred to the floor. The floor then transfers energy to the air above it.

This combination of passive and active solar systems will keep the home at a comfortable temperature during the fall competition, when temperatures will be dropping. But the heating system will also work very well all year long, once the home has reached its final destination. Not only will the system keep the home warm in the winter and cool in the summer, it will also provide hot water for showers, laundry, and dishes.

## Measuring Energy

How can we be sure that our solar collectors can transfer enough energy to the home to keep it warm enough in the winter? To answer that question, I need to explain how energy is measured.

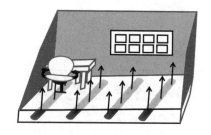

In the metric system, the unit for energy is the Joule. It takes 4.186 Joules to raise the temperature of one gram of water by one degree Celsius. The British and the Americans have their own unit for energy, the British Thermal Unit, or BTU. A BTU is the amount of energy required to raise the temperature of one pound of water by one degree Fahrenheit (°F). Of course, it's possible to convert between Joules and BTUs. One BTU is equal to 1,055 Joules. Most American engineers use BTUs when talking about heating systems.

As you know, fuels such as coal, oil, and natural gas store energy. These fuels release the stored energy when burned. In the table below, you can see the different energy content in BTUs for some common heating fuels.

| Fuel Source | Energy Content (BTUs) |
|---|---|
| Heating Oil | 140,000/gallon |
| Gasoline | 124,000/gallon |
| Wood (air-dried) | 8,000/pound |
| Coal | 24,000,000/ton |

When these fuels are burned, they release the stored energy. This energy is transferred by the heating system to the room air. Of course, heating systems are not perfectly efficient. You've probably heard and even used the word "efficiency" before, but what does it really mean? *Efficiency* is the comparison of energy inputs with respect to the useful outputs of a system. In an ideal system that is 100 percent efficient, the useful outputs are equal to the inputs.

But no system is 100 percent efficient. Not all of the energy contained in one gallon of heating oil—140,000 BTUs—is transferred to the room air. A certain amount of energy released from the heating oil will be transferred to places where it's not useful, such as the air around the boiler, the air around the pipes, the pipes, and the pumps. And it's possible that not all of the oil will burn completely.

To calculate the percent efficiency of this system, you need to determine the ratio of the useful output to the ideal output (which is equal to the input) and then multiply by 100. In a typical heating system, about 112,000 BTUs make it to the room air when a gallon of oil is burned.

> **Efficiency**
> is the comparison of energy input with respect to useful energy output of a system.
>
>
>
> In an ideal system that is 100 percent efficient, the useful output are equal to the input.
>
> $\uparrow = \downarrow$
>
> No system is 100 percent efficient!

$$\textbf{\textit{Efficiency}} \ (\eta) = \frac{useful\ output}{inputs}$$

Useful output: 112,000 BTUs  
Input: 140,000 BTUs

$$\textbf{\textit{\%Efficiency}} \ (\eta) = \frac{useful\ output}{inputs} \times 100$$

$$\textbf{\textit{\%Efficiency}} \ (\eta) = \frac{112,000\ BTUs}{140,000\ BTUs} \times 100$$

$$\textbf{\textit{\%Efficiency}} \ (\eta) = 80$$

So a typical oil heating system is 80 percent efficient.

## Is Solar Enough?

Will our "solar" systems keep our house warm enough? On a typical winter day, when temperatures hover around 30 degrees Fahrenheit, we may want the home to be about 40 degrees warmer than the outside temperature. Based on the volume of our home, we can calculate the amount of energy it will take to raise the temperature of that volume of air by 40 degrees. We estimate that it will take between 200,000 and 300,000 BTUs to do that.

Of course, we won't have to pump this many BTUs into the home each and every day. Most days we'll just have to make up for any energy that escapes the building through the walls, ceiling, or open doors and windows. Based on the insulation we've chosen and how air tight the house is, we estimate that we'll need to add about 45,000–50,000 BTUs of energy to the house every day to maintain a temperature that is 40 degrees higher than the outside air.

Our solar heating system can supply that amount of energy with no problem. On a sunny day, our solar collectors can heat water circulating through the system from 80 to 200 degrees Fahrenheit, a 120-degree difference. The piping-hot water is stored in the insulated 150-gallon tank. The fluid in the tank weighs about 2,500 pounds. Now, we know that when the temperature of one pound of water is increased by one degree F, the water has stored one BTU. After all, that's the definition of a BTU! When every pound of water in the tank has been heated 120 degrees, that gives us a total of 300,000 BTUs stored in the tank.

There will be some losses when that energy is transferred from the water through the floor pipes and into the room air. If we tried to transfer all of the energy in the water to the room air, only about 85 percent—or 255,000 BTUs—would actually make it. But that's still a lot more than we would need on a typical winter day. The tank can keep any unused water hot for a long time. So if we have a long stretch of gray days, we should still have plenty of energy to heat the home.

## Powering Up

Our home will need electric power so that its users can run their appliances, turn on lights, and plug in a computer or a stereo. During the day, large south-facing windows and skylights will maximize daylight so that the inhabitants will not need to turn on as many lights. But, of course, they'll need electric power if they want to see at night.

To solve this problem, we're equipping our home with photovoltaic (PV) panels. PV panels use the energy of the sun to generate electricity. The panels will be located on the roof next to the solar collectors. The PV panels should provide all of the power that the home's residents will need. During the day, the panels will generate more than enough electrical energy. The extra electricity will be stored in a battery. At night, the battery will be used to power the home.

## Down the Pipes

As soon as our home is in its final location, we'll connect it to the local municipality's water and sewerage system. But for the competition we must find another way to get clean water to the home and remove dirty water, or "gray water," as it's often called.

We will provide a 300-gallon tank of purified water that will act like a "water tower," pushing clean water to the home's taps. The tank will be on the ground floor, so we can't take advantage of gravity, which most reservoirs and water towers use to supply water to cities and towns. Instead, our tank will be pressurized. An electric pump, powered by the PV panels, will add air to the tank, which will compress the air space above the water and push the water through the pipes of the home.

We're connecting our home's drains, toilet, and laundry machine to another 300-gallon tank. This tank will be used to hold gray water. We don't plan to use toilets in the home during the competition. The people who empty the gray water tanks at the end of each day wouldn't appreciate that very much. But we do have to prove that our toilets are operational. We also have to be able to use the sinks, the washing machine, and then show that the wastewater drains out of our home. As soon as the competition is finished and our home is in its permanent position, we'll only need to hook up the sewerage, tap water, and electric connections.

## Look and Feel

How our house will look and feel is every bit as important as how it will function. No matter how energy-efficient our home is, its residents won't like living there if it isn't attractive and comfortable. While we've identified designs for our heating system, our electrical power system, and our water systems, we're only in the initial stages of developing the floor plan of the home.

Photovoltaic panels on a rooftop use energy from the sun to generate electricity.

Solar house built during the Solar Decathlon

Courtesy of Stefano Paltera/Solar Decathlon

That's why we're using a professional architecture firm called Clearwater Architects to provide advice as we design the house. The team has split into groups and brainstormed the most important features for a comfortable and attractive home. We've come up with a list of features that we'd like to incorporate in our ideal design. Our ideas include an eat-in kitchen, hardwood flooring in all rooms except the kitchen and bathroom, plenty of natural light (important for day lighting), and a nice, open layout. Of course, we may not be able to include all of these features in our design. This depends on cost and available materials.

## Communicating Our Solution

Last but not least, as part of the competition we will be judged on how well we communicate our solution. We've already built a website, which describes our process and what we've learned in more detail. We've written articles for our campus newspaper, contacted the media about our design, and shared our story with you through this textbook. We're also planning to give tours of the house on the National Mall. Communicating our solution is ongoing work. I'm constantly talking with classmates, friends, professors, and parents about what we're doing in hopes of raising public awareness of energy-efficient building design.

The "winner" of the solar decathlon gets a trophy for the best overall design. But, to be honest, I don't think anyone on the team really cares whether we win the trophy or not. We are all much more focused on using energy-efficient technologies to build a high-quality home for someone who needs it. In the meantime, we're all learning a tremendous amount about what it takes to build a home. Everyone who hears about our work, like you, is learning from our experience. So we all win. Now, that's the kind of competition I like!

*Engineering the Future: Science, Technology, and the Design Process*

Copyright © 2008 Museum of Science, Boston

##  What's the Story?

1. What are the two different sets of constraints that Lauren's team must consider when designing the house?

2. What is a passive solar heating system? Why is it called "passive"?

3. How does the team plan to communicate their solution?

##  Designing with Math and Science

4. Draw an energy diagram of the active solar heating system that includes the following: collector, pipes, sun, fluid, floor, and room air.

5. What's a BTU?

##  Connecting the Dots

6. Where should a thermal mass of a structure be located in order for passive solar heating to work well?

## What Do You Think?

7. You've been hired by an architecture firm as an energy efficiency specialist. As a first assignment, the firm has asked you to make a presentation in which you describe the attributes of an energy-efficient building. List the attributes having to do with the location, the architectural design, the construction material, and the heating system of the building.

8. Look at the table of common fuel sources shown in Lauren's story. Do you think these are equivalent quantities? How does this affect how someone might support using one type of fuel versus another? Work with a partner to calculate how many pounds of wood would need to be burned to equal the energy content in a ton of coal or a gallon of heating oil.

## Going with the Flow

# 17

## *In Deep*

### Bob Brown

*Courtesy of John Ost*

### 🔧 Key Concepts
#### from Previous Chapters

**14**   Stress($\sigma$) = $F/A$

**14**   Strain($\varepsilon$) = $\Delta L/L$

**15**   Differences drive change

**15**   Energy travels from areas of high concentration to areas of lower concentration

Scientists rely on technologies to help them investigate the natural world, whether they are exploring the vastness of outer space or the microscopic contents of a single cell. Engineers create these technologies by relying on principles and natural laws developed by scientists.

I understand the relationship between scientists and engineers well. My name is Bob Brown, and I am a design engineer at Woods Hole Oceanographic Institution (WHOI), an ocean research organization based in Massachusetts. For years, I was also a pilot on the Alvin, the United States' only deep-sea diving submersible vehicle that carries passengers. The Alvin can dive to depths of 4,500 meters—that's 14,764 feet!—and has made over 4,000 dives in its long, illustrious career.

The Alvin has surveyed the sunken ship *Titanic,* explored the first hydrothermal vents ever discovered in the Pacific Ocean, and even located a hydrogen bomb accidentally dropped in the Mediterranean Sea.

As its pilot, I've seen some amazing sights on the ocean floor and have watched as scientists discovered new life forms, such as bacteria that feed on sulfur produced by deep thermal vents. Discoveries like these have led space scientists to rethink what kinds of life may be possible on other planets.

The Alvin has given marine scientists an invaluable tool. But like any technology, it's not perfect. I'm now working to redesign Alvin so it can go deeper and explore some of the most remote regions on Earth—places humans have never seen.

## A High-Pressure Environment

Designing a submersible vehicle requires an understanding of the conditions it is likely to experience at the bottom of the ocean. The redesigned Alvin must be able to withstand very, very high pressure.

*Pressure* is defined as force per unit area. Pressure and stress have a similar definition and meaning, and the terms are used interchangeably. However, scientists and engineers tend to use the term *pressure* when describing the force exerted by a contained fluid. A *fluid* is a substance that flows easily, such as a liquid or a gas. The pressure from a fluid might be exerted on the walls of a container or on an object submerged in it. For example, the water in a fish tank exerts an outward pressure on the aquarium walls. Similarly, the walls of a toy submarine submerged in an aquarium are also subjected to water pressure, because the force exerted by the fluid is perpendicular to every surface it contacts.

To get a feeling for differences in pressure, imagine two soccer balls filled with air. One ball is filled with a small amount of air, so it is easy to squeeze. The second ball is packed with so much air that it is very firm. The air inside of each soccer ball is pushing against the inner wall. However, the air in the second ball is pushing with greater force per unit area. If you were to measure the air pressure inside each ball, you would find that the firmer one would have the higher pressure.

1. Water in tank exerts **outward** pressure on the walls of the container.

2. Water in tank exerts **inward** pressure on the walls of the **submerged object.**

1st ball: small amount of air

2nd ball: packed with air

Air in our atmosphere and water in the ocean, or any other body of water contained in our atmosphere, also have a measurable pressure. Air pressure is due largely to the weight of all the air molecules above us in the atmosphere pushing down against the Earth's surface. At sea level, you experience the force of all this air at a pressure of 14.7 PSI (pounds per square inch). If you went to Denver, Colorado, which is at higher altitude, you would find that the air pressure is only 12.2 PSI. That's because there is less air above Denver pushing down.

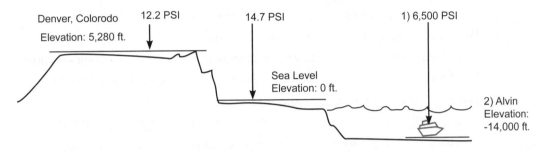

Denver, Colorodo
Elevation: 5,280 ft.

12.2 PSI

14.7 PSI

1) 6,500 PSI

Sea Level
Elevation: 0 ft.

2) Alvin
Elevation:
-14,000 ft.

If, instead of going to Denver, you were to dive into the sea, you would experience increasing pressure due to the weight of the seawater above you—plus the weight of all the air in the atmosphere above the sea! The deeper you dive, the more water you have above you, and, in turn, the greater the pressure. A general rule of thumb is that fluid pressure in the ocean increases about fifteen PSI for every thirty feet you dive.

We want the new Alvin to reach even deeper depths, more than 21,000 feet below sea level. As we redesign Alvin, we are assuming that the submersible will be operating at a maximum water pressure of about 9,700 PSI. That's a fluid pressure over 600 times greater than the pressure the submersible will experience on the surface! To fortify the Alvin's replacement against the massive pressure it will experience, we must make the structure very strong; otherwise it could suffer a catastrophic failure, resulting in the loss of the craft and the crew.

The Alvin's replacement must be made out of material that has enough strength to endure the demanding pressure at its depth limit. After researching the available materials, we chose a titanium alloy, which is extremely lightweight and strong—so strong that the walls of the Alvin's replacement will need to be only about three inches thick. The oxygen content of the material is quite low—another advantage from our point of view. The low oxygen content will help prevent the material from reacting with seawater to form corrosion.

When there is a **fluid pressure difference,** fluid will flow from the area of higher fluid pressure to the area of lower fluid pressure until there is no difference, unless something gets in the way.

Designing the structure would be fairly straightforward if Alvin's replacement did not have windows or a door. These hull openings must be designed so they seal very tight to prevent leakage. We test the seals around the windows and doors extensively. Even a small leak would flood the submersible quickly, due to the enormous pressure difference between the water outside the Alvin (seawater) and the air pressure inside. This *fluid pressure difference* will force the fluid to move from the higher-pressure area to the lower-pressure area until there is no difference or unless something gets in the way.

What would happen to the air already inside the Alvin if a leak did occur? The water flooding into the submersible would begin to exert pressure on the trapped air. As more water entered, the increasing pressure would compress the air into a smaller and smaller volume. Gases, like air, are *compressible* fluids. The empty space between gas molecules is quite large, which allows the pressure to squeeze the molecules together. Under increased pressure, the gas occupies a smaller volume, but its mass stays the same. Liquids, on the other hand, are essentially *incompressible,* because applying pressure to a liquid will not significantly change its volume. So even though the air would not be escaping, the Alvin would still fill up with water.

## To Sink or Swim

One of the systems aboard the Alvin's replacement uses the compressibility of gases to make the submersible descend to the ocean floor and ascend back to the surface. The Alvin weighs just over eighteen tons, and its replacement will weigh nearly as much. You might think that these submersibles would sink like stones to the ocean floor, but they don't. In fact, the Alvin would never reach the ocean floor if we didn't help it.

○ **Fluids in a Syringe** ○

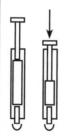

### Compressible

If you push the piston of a capped syringe filled with **air,** you can compress the air inside the syringe to a smaller volume.

This is because air is a compressible fluid.

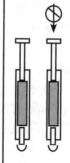

### Incompressible

If you try to push the piston of a capped syringe filled with **water,** you can't compress the water inside the syringe into a smaller volume.

This is because liquids are an incompressible fluid.

*Engineering the Future: Science, Technology, and the Design Process*

Any object immersed in fluid experiences a ***buoyant force*** that pushes it upward. Because pressure increases with depth, the pressure on Alvin's lower surface (bottom) will always be higher than its upper surface (top), pushing it upward. The buoyant force on an object in a fluid is equal to weight of the volume of fluid that is displaced.

So how does *anything* sink? While the buoyant force pushes up on a submerged object, the weight of the object pulls it down. If the volume of an object weighs more than the volume of water it displaces, it sinks. If the buoyant force and the weight of the object are equal, the object will be ***neutrally buoyant.*** A neutrally buoyant object won't move up or down unless another force acts on it.

Engineers make submersibles descend or ascend by adjusting either the weight or the displacement volume of a submersible. To dive to the sea floor, the "original" Alvin carries steel weights. With the steel weights, the Alvin's total weight is greater than the buoyant force, so it submerges. When the Alvin arrives at its destination depth, the pilot drops some of the weights onto the sea floor, making the Alvin neutrally buoyant. The pilot can then use the Alvin's thrusters to maneuver near the ocean floor, allowing scientists on board to make observations and collect samples. By dropping the remaining weights, the Alvin becomes more buoyant, allowing it to return to the surface.

Back when the original Alvin was being designed, in the 1950s, people were not so concerned about leaving steel weights on the sea floor. That attitude has changed. We now know that the steel weights can actually alter the communities of living organisms on which they fall by changing the chemistry of the water surrounding them.

The ***buoyant force,*** the upward push on the object, equals the weight of the volume of water displaced by an object.

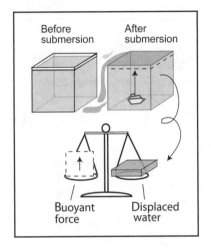

Before submersion / After submersion

Buoyant force | Displaced water

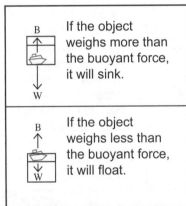

B / W — If the object weighs more than the buoyant force, it will sink.

B / W — If the object weighs less than the buoyant force, it will float.

Underwater images taken by Alvin

The Alvin, operated by Woods Hole Oceanographic Institute engineers, is the nation's only deep-diving sub that carries passengers.

## Vehicle Depth Control with VBS

Tank is filled with air and **no water.**

Vehicle is on the **surface.**

Water is pumped into tank; **air** in tank **compresses.**

Vehicle **sinks.**

Some water is pumped out of the tanks; **air** inside tank **expands.**

Vehicle acquires **neutral buoyancy.**

Water is pumped out of the tank; the **air expands** to the **full volume** of tank.

The vehicle **rises** to the surface.

As we design a replacement for the Alvin, we're developing a system for diving that does not use weights at all. It's called the Variable Ballast System (VBS). The system will be a larger-scale version of a system already used on the Alvin to fine-tune its buoyancy as soon as the vehicle has arrived at its destination depth. In Alvin's replacement, the VBS will be used for ascent and descent as well. No more steel weights!

Take a look at the steps used by the Variable Ballast System on the left. Seawater is pumped into and out of spherical tanks located at the front and rear of the submersible. The spherical tanks are hollow, and their volume is fixed. When we're floating at the surface, the spheres contain air. To dive, we pump water into the spheres, without removing any of the air. As the spheres fill with water, the air in the spheres compresses, taking up less volume. Pumping water into the spheres increases the weight of the submersible without increasing its displacement volume.

After we have reached our destination on the sea floor, we pump some water out of the tanks to achieve neutral buoyancy. As we pump water out, the air inside the tanks expands, taking up the volume of the tank not filled by water. When it's time to ascend back to the surface, we make the submersible lighter by pumping more water out of the tanks, and the submersible returns to the surface.

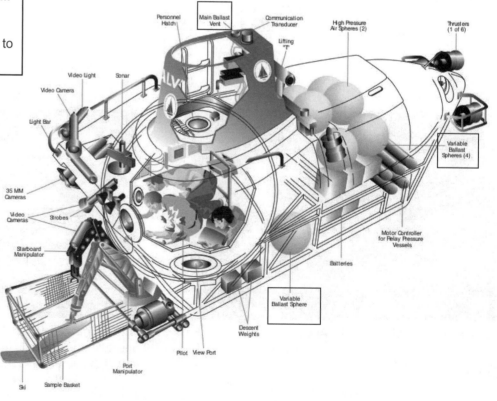

*Engineering the Future: Science, Technology, and the Design Process*

# A Strong Arm

Much like the Alvin, the replacement submersible will be equipped with an arm that can reach out and pick up specimens of rock, sediment, or marine life. The arm will then place the specimen in a storage basket on the side or front of the submersible, where it will be stored until the submersible surfaces and scientists can collect it.

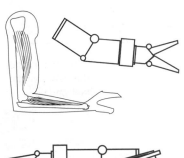

The arm is modeled after a human arm with a shoulder joint, an elbow joint, and a wrist joint. And like a human arm, the Alvin's arm has seven degrees of freedom—meaning the arm can move in seven different ways.

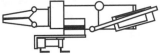

Use your own arm to get an idea of what is meant by degrees of freedom. First, extend your arm straight out so it is parallel to the ground with your palm facing the floor. Keep your arm straight, and then move it from the shoulder. You'll notice that you can move it three ways: vertically, horizontally, and rotationally, as if you were turning a knob. Your shoulder joint has three degrees of freedom.

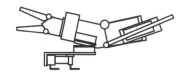

Now move your arm from the elbow only, holding your shoulder joint fixed. Your elbow joint moves vertically, but not horizontally and not rotationally. Your elbow has only one degree of freedom. Now move only your wrist. You'll see that, like your shoulder, your wrist has three degrees of freedom, even though horizontal and rotational movement of the wrist is limited. (In fact, most of the rotational movement takes place along your arm below the elbow.)

The arm on the Alvin also has seven degrees of freedom, and for that reason, it can move much like a human arm moves. But, of course, muscles don't move Alvin's arm. Instead, a hydraulic power system serves as the "muscles." *Hydraulic systems* use liquid to transmit power by taking advantage of fluid characteristics and pressure changes.

Several kinds of hydraulic systems exist, but the diagram on the following page illustrates a hydraulic system similar to the one used to move Alvin's arm. The hydraulic system is filled with a liquid, usually oil or water. This liquid is often called the *working fluid.* A pump increases the pressure of the working fluid in one part of the system, by pushing on it. This force creates a difference in pressure between the fluid on one side of the piston and a fluid on the other side of the piston. Remember that a fluid flows from the region of higher pressure to the region of lower pressure until there is no difference, or unless something gets in the way. In this system, the piston is "in the way," but because it is not fixed, it is pushed by the flowing fluid. As shown in the diagram, the handle controls which way the piston moves by changing which side of the piston is higher pressure and which side is lower pressure.

## Handle at Pulled Position

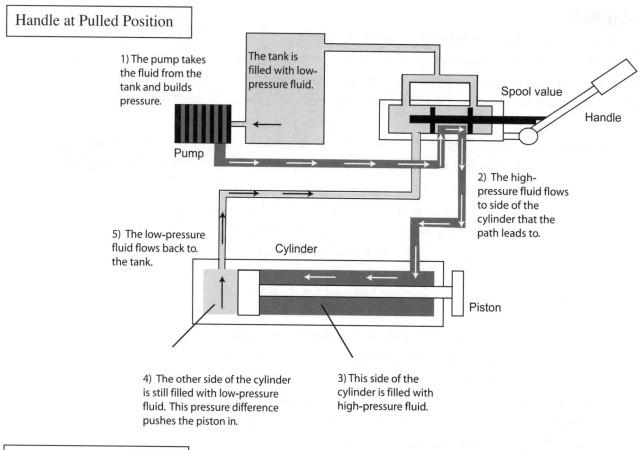

1) The pump takes the fluid from the tank and builds pressure.

The tank is filled with low-pressure fluid.

Spool value

Handle

Pump

2) The high-pressure fluid flows to side of the cylinder that the path leads to.

5) The low-pressure fluid flows back to the tank.

Cylinder

Piston

4) The other side of the cylinder is still filled with low-pressure fluid. This pressure difference pushes the piston in.

3) This side of the cylinder is filled with high-pressure fluid.

## Handle at Pushed Position

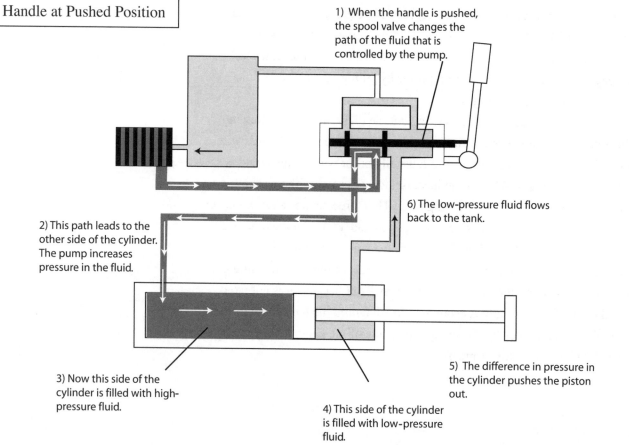

1) When the handle is pushed, the spool valve changes the path of the fluid that is controlled by the pump.

2) This path leads to the other side of the cylinder. The pump increases pressure in the fluid.

6) The low-pressure fluid flows back to the tank.

3) Now this side of the cylinder is filled with high-pressure fluid.

4) This side of the cylinder is filled with low-pressure fluid.

5) The difference in pressure in the cylinder pushes the piston out.

In Unit 2, you learned about thermal systems—or systems that make objects get hotter or colder by transferring energy. In this unit, you'll learn about systems that make things move—such as hydraulic systems. When energy is transferred through a system so that an object moves, the system is doing **work** on the object. Now, you can understand why the fluid in a hydraulic system is called a "working" fluid; it is transferring energy from the input of a system to the output of a system.

Consider these energy diagrams.

Heating System

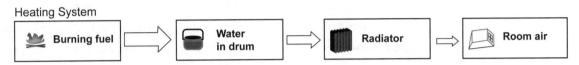

The diagram above illustrates a heating system, while the diagram below depicts the Alvin's hydraulic system. When the Alvin's hydraulic arm picks up a rock on the sea floor, it is transferring energy to move the rock. The motion of the rock tells you the arm is doing work on the rock.

Hydraulic System

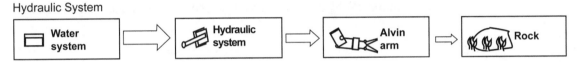

With hydraulic "muscles," the arm can lift objects that weigh as much as 200 pounds. How much energy is being transferred from the Alvin's arm to the rock? The amount of energy transferred can be calculated using the following equation:

| $W = Fd$ | $W$ = Energy transferred<br>$F$ = Force on the object<br>$d$ = distance traveled |
| --- | --- |

Where $W$ (for work) is the energy transferred, $F$ is the force on the object, and $d$ is the distance traveled by the object.

If Alvin's arm were to pick up a twenty-pound rock and lift it five feet off the sea floor, how much energy would be transferred?

$W = Fd$

$W = 20$ lb. $\times$ 5 ft.

$W = 100$ ft. lb.

| $F = 20$ lb.<br>$d = 5$ ft. | Foot-Pounds (ft.lb.) is the English unit for work. |
| --- | --- |

Engineers have designed many systems that do work: elevators, car lifts, cars, airplanes, ski lifts, to name only a few examples. Any technology that applies a force to move something is doing work! You'll explore several of these systems in this unit.

As we design a replacement for the Alvin, we're working to make the hydraulic arm easier to use. In the original Alvin, an operator would have to manually flip switches controlling the hydraulic system for each piston. This manual work made operating the arm very time-consuming. (To see why, try picking up an object by moving only one joint in your arm in one direction at a time!) The Alvin's replacement will use a different system to control the arm. Inside the cockpit of the Alvin, there will be a small-scale version of the arm. The operator will only have to grasp the hand of the arm and move it the way he or she wants the hydraulic arm to move. A computer system will calculate the coordinates of the small-scale arm and will activate the hydraulic system as necessary to move the large arm until it achieves the same orientation as the smaller one.

The Alvin has served us well during its many years of service and has given us great insight into life at the bottom of the ocean, as well as into the features the ideal submersible might have. No doubt the replacement for the Alvin will teach us even more—both about deep ocean ecosystems and about submersible design!

 ## What's the Story?

1. List three systems on the Alvin that Bob's team is planning to redesign for the Alvin's replacement.

2. How is the Alvin an example of the relationship between engineers and scientists?

 ## Designing with Math and Science

3. Imagine that you've just inflated a kick ball and are holding the air in the ball with your finger over the opening. What happens when you remove your finger and the air can pass freely through the opening? Explain why this happens in terms of pressure difference and fluid movement.

4. How is the compressibility of gases used in a designed system described in this chapter? How is the incompressibility of liquids used in a different designed system described in this chapter?

5. A hydraulic system in the elbow joint of the Alvin is pressurized so that there is a pressure difference of 20 PSI between the working fluid on one side of a piston and the working fluid on the other side. What is the surface area of the piston if it is pushed with a force large enough to lift a five-pound rock? (Remember: $P=F/A$)

 ## What Do You Think?

6. Pneumatic systems are similar to hydraulic systems, but they use a gas, such as air, as a working fluid. Conduct library or Internet research, and write a description of a technology that uses a pneumatic system. How is the pneumatic system designed to work using pressure differences? How is the fact that gases are compressible incorporated into the design?

7. Develop and sketch a design for a robotic arm that can pick up a paper cup. Will your robotic arm be moved by a hydraulic or pneumatic system? Why?

# 18

## *Shooting for the Moon*

### Aprille Ericsson

Courtesy of Aprille Joy Ericsson

### Key Concepts
#### from Previous Chapters

2 Engineering Design Process

2 Testing and Evaluating

11 Thermal Expansion

17 Fluids

17 Pressure

17 Working and Work

In the next decade, if all goes as planned, a spacecraft developed by NASA may bring dust from Mars back to Earth for the first time. These tiny pieces of dust, from the Martian surface and throughout its atmosphere, could reveal secrets about the red planet's past and future—including its potential to sustain life.

Sound exciting? I think so too. I'm Dr. Aprille Joy Ericsson, and I'm an astronautical engineer at NASA's Goddard Space Flight Center in Maryland. Astronautical engineering is a branch of engineering concerned with creating new technologies to explore specific areas. Right now, I'm developing a proposal for the SCIM mission. SCIM stands for Sample Collection for the Investigation of Mars. NASA missions are large projects that involve hundreds of engineers and scientists, as well as some of the most cutting-edge technologies of our time.

The SCIM mission involves not only designing the spacecraft, but also planning the entire journey of the spacecraft. This planning includes the design of all supporting technology. My team must choose a launch vehicle, develop a feedback and control system for maneuvering the spacecraft, determine the route to and from Mars, and decide how the spacecraft will relay information to scientists and engineers back on Earth. These are a few of many, many complex design decisions.

The SCIM mission is a massive design project, but that's exactly why I find it so appealing. As an astronautical engineer, I must challenge myself constantly to aim high—literally. I first caught the aerospace bug in a summer program after my junior year in high school. I visited an air force base in New Hampshire, where I got to sit in the control tower and fly in a flight simulator—and I received a pilot's score! From then on, I wanted to design technologies that fly. I attended the Massachusetts Institute of Technology (MIT), where I received a degree in aeronautical/astronautical engineering.

When I graduated in the early 1980s, most aerospace engineering jobs were for strategic defense, which meant my future job probably would have required me to develop missiles. I carefully considered how that work might impact society and decided not to apply for those jobs. Instead, I went back to school and became the first female to earn a doctorate in mechanical engineering from Howard University, a historically black college in Washington, D.C. My specialty in aerospace helped me get a job as an astronautical engineer at NASA's Goddard Space Flight Center. I have worked my way through a variety of missions.

*Courtesy of Aprille Joy Ericsson*

## Mars Scout

proposal I'm working on is very exciting, and I truly hope be selected for funding. The process for selection is very NASA starts by issuing an "Announcement of Opportunity" This document invites teams of researchers, scientists, and from universities, industries, government, and nongovernment organizations all over the world to submit proposals for a an engineering design challenge.

*Engineering the Future: Science, Technology, and the Design Process*

The AO lists the mission requirements, sets constraints on how much the mission can cost, and estimates a completion date. Teams submit very detailed proposals, and a few teams receive funding to flesh out their ideas, which may mean constructing and testing a prototype. Only a few teams are chosen as finalists to receive enough funding to design and complete their proposed missions.

Right now, I'm developing the first proposal for the SCIM. I can't share all of the details, but I can give you an idea how my team of engineers and scientists is working to solve the problem.

The original AO asked for proposals for "Mars Scouts." The Scout could be a Mars-orbiting spacecraft that takes remote observations; a spacecraft that lands on the planet and uses instruments to study the Martian atmosphere, surface, or subsurface; or a spacecraft that lands on Mars, collects samples, and returns them to Earth. The total cost of each Mars Scout mission—from launch to landing—must be under $4.5 million. The spacecraft is set to launch by December 31, 2011.

As you can see, the challenge is open-ended. Many possible solutions could meet the criteria and constraints it outlines—and many teams will submit proposals. To be selected, my team must make a strong case that our mission will give scientists an invaluable tool that will perform optimally throughout the entire mission.

We believe the SCIM will practically sell itself. That's because no samples of Martian material have ever been brought back to Earth for study. What could Mars dust tell us? The dust particles found on Mars may hold important clues about the age and composition of rocks on Mars. They may also carry telltale markers of current or past life. Without bringing the samples back to Earth so scientists can analyze them, we probably won't ever know what information Mars has to share.

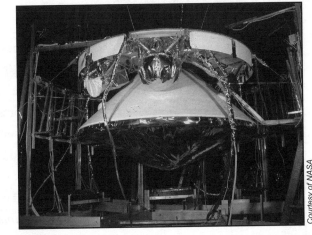

Courtesy of NASA

Mars Rover

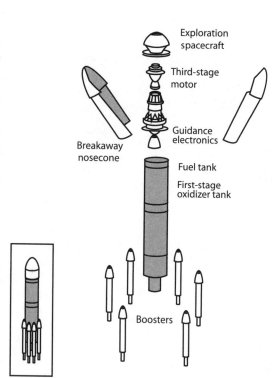

Exploration spacecraft

Third-stage motor

Guidance electronics

Breakaway nosecone

Fuel tank

First-stage oxidizer tank

Boosters

## The Mission: From Earth to Mars and Back Again

Our proposed mission will use a launch vehicle to lift the spacecraft into the Earth's upper atmosphere, which starts over fifty-three miles above the Earth's surface. The launch vehicle is a very large-scale version of the toy rockets you might find at a science shop. At launch, a rocket engine burns fuel and, in an amazing cloud of burning gases, leaves the launch pad and races toward outer space. Within minutes, the rocket travels at speeds exceeding 13,000 miles per hour. The first stage of the launch vehicle will carry the SCIM into the upper atmosphere; once there, the first-stage rocket falls away from the spacecraft, burning up as it reenters the Earth's atmosphere.

A second-stage rocket attached to the SCIM spacecraft will fire after the first-stage rocket has fallen away. This rocket will propel the SCIM spacecraft even farther into space; then it will fall away. After leaving the Earth's atmosphere, the spacecraft will continue moving along its flight path toward the red planet. The spacecraft will move at speeds of approximately two miles per second, firing onboard thrusters to adjust its direction. But even at this speed, the vehicle's journey to Mars and back to Earth will take about four years.

### Editor's Note
## Rocket Science

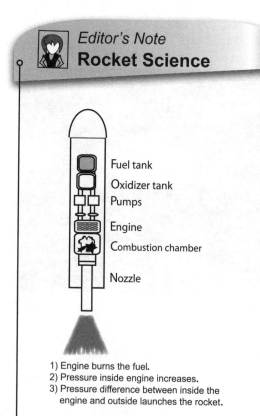

Fuel tank

Oxidizer tank

Pumps

Engine

Combustion chamber

Nozzle

1) Engine burns the fuel.
2) Pressure inside engine increases.
3) Pressure difference between inside the engine and outside launches the rocket.

How does a launch vehicle accelerate a spacecraft to speeds greater than 13,000 miles per hour in just minutes? The engine makes this feat possible. An **engine** is a system that uses temperature differences to create pressure differences. These pressure differences can be harnessed to do useful work. Just how engines are designed to do this work will be explored later in this unit.

One commonly used launch vehicle, the Delta 2 rocket, burns highly refined kerosene. On launch, fuel and liquid oxygen are pumped into the **combustion chamber** of the rocket, where they combine and burn explosively. The expanding gases from the intense, continuous burning of fuel enormously increase the pressure in the combustion chamber. The hot gases from the burning fuel escape through a small opening, called the **nozzle,** at a very high speed. The mass of these gases escapes from the nozzle, propelling the rocket and its contents forward toward outer space.

*Engineering the Future: Science, Technology, and the Design Process*

Why this occurs is explained by Isaac Newton's Third Law of Motion, which states that every action has an equal and opposite reaction. The direction of the push on the first object is opposite to the direction of the push on the second object. We can use this law to describe why the rocket moves forward. As the rocket pushes gases in one direction, the rocket is pushed in the opposite direction.

Make your own rocket by blowing up a balloon and pinching the neck closed. When you let go of the balloon's neck, the balloon "rockets" around the room. In this case, the balloon acts like the combustion chamber of a rocket, pushing gases through the tiny neck of the balloon.

Action                    Reaction

According to Newton's third law, the air pushed out of the balloon is the "action" and the forward movement of the balloon is the "reaction."

Engineers must design rocket engines with enough thrust to lift the rocket and its contents against the force of gravity. **Thrust** is the force or action that causes the reaction of the rocket's forward movement. Thrust is measured using the rate mass is ejected from the nozzle, the velocity of the escaping gas, and the pressure at the nozzle exit. To adjust how much thrust an engine has, engineers alter how rapidly the fuel in the engine is burned, the size of the combustion chamber, and the diameter of the nozzle. All of these factors determine how fast the hot gasses are ejected from the nozzle, which affects the amount of thrust. Of course, real engines don't always behave exactly as expected, so it's necessary to build a prototype and measure the actual thrust of the new engine before it's used to lift a rocket into space.

In outer space, spacecraft often use onboard thrusters to change their direction. These thrusters work like small rocket engines joined to the spacecraft that can be fired to give the vehicle a push now and then to correct its direction.

> **Newton's Third Law of Motion:**
>
> Every action has an equal and opposite reaction.
>
> The (mass × acceleration) of the gas ejected from the rocket engine backward = the (mass × acceleration) of the rocket forward. "Acceleration" is the scientific term for speeding up.

# Resistance-Free Travel

After it leaves Earth's atmosphere, the SCIM spacecraft will travel at a high speed toward its rendezvous with Mars without burning fuel, except when it uses thrusters to adjust its position. So, how does it keep moving? To answer that question, let's consider our own experience with moving objects on Earth.

Every moving object on Earth meets resistance of some sort. *Resistance* opposes movement. Wad up a sheet of paper and see how far you can throw it. You'll see that it will slow down and drop to the ground. As it moves, it bumps into air particles, which slow it down. But in space, there is no air and, therefore, no air resistance. If you threw the wad of paper in outer space, it would keep going forever unless something got in its way. That's Newton's first law: "An object in uniform motion will continue in uniform motion unless acted on by an outside force."

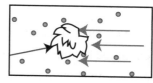 

This law explains why spacecraft don't need to burn fuel continuously in space to move forward the way cars or airplanes do here on Earth. After a spacecraft has left the Earth's atmosphere and has entered the air-resistance-free environment of space, it travels at the same speed.

When planning a route for the Mars SCIM, we must consider how gravity will affect the spacecraft. Even after it leaves Earth's atmosphere, the spacecraft will still be affected by Earth's gravity. Remember that the moon stays in its orbit due to its gravitational attraction to the Earth, so the influence of Earth's gravity extends far into space. However, as the craft gets farther away from Earth, the strength of the Earth's gravitational pull decreases. At this point, the sun's gravity becomes more important. Gravitational attraction is directly proportional to a body's mass. The sun is 333,000 times as massive as Earth, so its gravity is 333,000 times stronger. In fact, we must consider the gravitational attraction of the Earth, sun, moon, and Mars to determine what path the spacecraft will take.

There are two Mars Rovers that have already made the trip to Mars: Spirit and Opportunity. The following diagram shows the flight path of the Mars Rover Opportunity, which was launched in 2003. The Mars Rover left Earth's atmosphere and entered into an orbit around the sun. It was scheduled to fire its thrusters six times to fine-tune its orbit. NASA made calculations accurate enough that the thrusters only needed to be fired three times. When the spacecraft came close enough to Mars, the planet's gravity pulled it in for a landing.

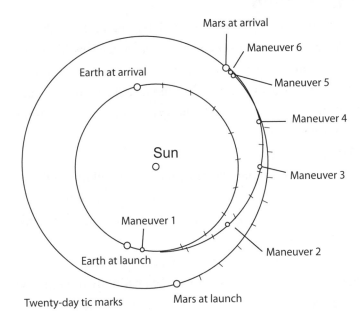

Mars at arrival

Maneuver 6

Maneuver 5

Earth at arrival

Maneuver 4

Sun
○

Maneuver 3

Maneuver 1

Maneuver 2

Earth at launch

Twenty-day tic marks

Mars at launch

The diagram shows the original flight path of the another Mars-bound spacecraft, the Mars Rover Opportunity, which was launched in 2003. According to the diagram, the Mars Rover left Earth's atmosphere and entered orbit around the sun. It was scheduled to fire its thrusters six times to "tweak" its orbit, in order to swing close to Mars. However, only three were needed. When the spacecraft came close enough to Mars, the red planet's gravity pulled it in for a landing.

## The Low Pass

After the SCIM reaches Mars, it will enter Mars' atmosphere and pass as close as twenty-three miles above the planet's surface for about one minute. To collect samples of Martian material, the SCIM spacecraft will open side panels to expose panels made from "aerogel," a very low-density, sticky gelatinous substance. Think of it as a clear, lightweight Jell-O. As the spacecraft flies through the dusty Martian atmosphere, pieces of dust will be trapped and preserved in the aerogel panels. Besides collecting dust particles, the SCIM spacecraft will also measure the concentration of dust in the atmosphere, collect gas samples, and take photographs.

After completing its mission, the spacecraft will fire its thrusters once again. The SCIM will accelerate to a higher altitude, leaving the Martian atmosphere behind, and begin orbiting the planet. The spacecraft will swing around the planet; then, at the appropriate orientation, the spacecraft will fire its thrusters to break free of Mars' gravity and begin its long trip back to Earth. Upon returning, the SCIM will be captured by Earth's gravity. Slowing its descent by firing its thrusters, the spacecraft will use a parachute to gently land at a predetermined location. I'll be waiting with other scientists and engineers ready to meet it.

## Minimizing the Potential for Failure: Testing and Evaluating

Because we will be bringing back samples from Mars, and there is a chance, however remote, that these samples may contain living organisms, we must make sure that we do not contaminate the Earth. An extraterrestrial life form could escape and pose a danger to life on Earth. To minimize risk, we're designing a system that retracts the aerogel panels into the spacecraft's interior. During the return trip, these panels will be baked at temperatures higher than living organisms can tolerate.

I've been working on engineering the mechanism that will retract the panels into the ship's interior. What happens if the mechanism fails to fully retract the panels? Well, because it would be impossible to bake the samples, we wouldn't be able to let the SCIM land on Earth.

This is just one example of a system failure that could threaten the success of the multi-million-dollar mission. To minimize the possibility of failure, we always include some backup systems that will operate in case the primary system fails. Of course, we can't include too many backup systems, as each one adds weight and cost.

Because our backup options are limited, we'll conduct many tests ahead of time to make sure the spacecraft will perform its tasks during the mission. This testing means simulating some of the extreme conditions of outer space. For instance, we know that the SCIM spacecraft will experience dramatic temperature fluctuations. Outer space can be very cold, because there is no air to absorb and store warmth from sunlight. However, when the spacecraft is in direct sunlight, the sunny side may heat up to very high temperatures. These dramatic temperature differences can cause materials to deform. To make sure our materials will perform they way we expect them to, we must test them under very high and very low temperatures.

Here on Earth, our atmosphere protects us from high-energy space particles called *cosmic rays.* Without protection from the atmosphere, the spacecraft will be bombarded by this radiation. High levels of radiation can cause certain materials—such as electronics or solar cells—to degrade. While it's possible to shield devices on the spacecraft that are particularly prone to radiation damage with special materials, these protections add weight and increase costs. So we subject the spacecraft components to high levels of radiation to determine which components are in danger and how much protection they need.

Changes in pressure pose another problem. While on Earth, the spacecraft is subjected to the pressure of the atmosphere; but in space, air pressure is so low that it's negligible. This tremendous pressure difference can cause problems for some components, such as the fuel tank that will be needed for mid-course corrections. We can design the tank so that it adjusts its internal pressure during launch, but we can't be sure it will work unless we test it in a vacuum chamber where we can simulate the types of pressure changes the spacecraft is likely to experience on its journey.

These are just a few of the many tests we plan to conduct on the prototype. As soon as the spacecraft is launched, there is very little we can do to repair it should a system fail. We have to get it right the first time. This means troubleshooting and optimizing the prototype until we have great confidence the spacecraft will operate as expected.

As you can imagine, a successful mission requires significant planning and hard work. It also means coming up with new and innovative ideas. Engineers play a very important role at NASA. It's a common misconception that NASA employs mostly scientists. In fact, NASA employs ten times as many engineers as scientists.

When working on projects like this one, I like to keep in mind one of my favorite quotes: "Shoot for the moon, and if you miss, you'll still be among the stars." These words help me keep perspective. Every new proposal we work on here at NASA is "shooting for the moon." After all, we're proposing technologies that have never before existed and may make invaluable contributions to science. Even when a proposal I've submitted is not selected, the ideas my team developed are not wasted. Chances are good that the ideas will be incorporated into other future missions. Most importantly, I've had the satisfaction of working with people here and all over the world who are as full of passion and motivation as I am. So I'm already among the stars.

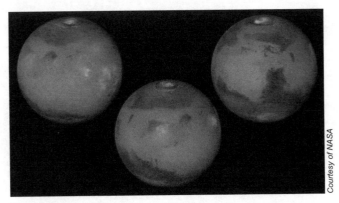
Three views of Mars

##  What's the Story?

1. Why is it important that the Mars SCIM may bring dust from the Martian atmosphere back to Earth?

2. How will the engineers on Dr. Ericsson's team test the spacecraft before it is launched?

## Designing with Math and Science

3. What is Newton's Third Law? Use it to explain how a rocket engine propels a spacecraft into outer space.

4. Why must the engineers like Dr. Ericsson consider pressure differences when designing components such as the fuel tank? Explain your answer in terms of fluid movement and pressure differences.

5. What is meant by the term "resistance"? Explain a scenario in which you have experienced fluid resistance.

## What Do You Think?

6. Describe at least three other technologies that use Newton's Third Law.

# 19

# *Fuel from the Fields*

## Joshua Tickell

*Courtesy of Fred Greaves*

### ⚙ Key Concepts
**from Previous Chapters**

- ② Communicating the Solution (EDP)
- ⑦ Life Cycle Analysis
- ⑮ Temperature
- ⑮ Energy Transfer and Storage
- ⑰ Working Fluid
- ⑰ Pressure

My dad introduced me to the two greatest loves of my life: French fries and fast cars. I never could have known growing up that my two loves would take me so far—25,000 miles and counting.

My name is Joshua Tickell. I've spent two years driving across the United States in a van powered by biodiesel—fuel made from recycled French fry grease that I collected for free at McDonald's, Long John Silver's, and Burger King along my journey.

How did I get that idea? As I said, I've always loved driving and eating fast food. It wasn't until I got to college at New College in Sarasota, Florida, that I realized how much cars contribute to serious environmental and public health problems.

Most cars and trucks in this country burn diesel fuel or gasoline, which are both made from oil. Oil, along with natural gas and coal, is what's called a "fossil fuel." Fossil fuels are so-named because they formed hundreds of millions of years ago during the time of the dinosaurs. Most likely, these fuels started forming when dead and decaying plants collected in the bottom of swamps and waterways and, over time, were covered with sand and silt. That sand and silt eventually hardened into heavy layers of rock, which applied pressure on the decaying plant material. As centuries passed, high temperatures and pressure converted the plant matter to crude oil, coal, or natural gas.

Fossil fuels store a lot of energy, which they release when burned. But using fossil fuels has led to many problems. The burning of fossil fuels produces carbon dioxide and nitrous oxide gases. These gases trap energy from the sun and hold it near the Earth's surface—a phenomenon called the "Greenhouse Effect." Many scientists believe that our society's increased use of fossil fuels is raising the Earth's temperature. Some even predict that global warming will cause serious climate change and raise the sea level—both of which may have devastating effects on coastal cities and agricultural systems—sometime in the next century. According to the Environmental Protection Agency, the United States produces almost 6.6 tons of greenhouse gases per person every year, 82 percent of these gases resulting from burning fossil fuels to generate electricity or power our cars.

Extracting and transporting fossil fuels pose other serious problems. Because oil, natural gas, and coal are located deep under the Earth's surface, people must build complex systems of wells, mines, pipelines, and roadways—often in pristine environments—to extract them. Habitat loss and degradation in some of the most beautiful natural places on Earth are the results of collecting fossil fuels.

Likewise, transporting oil in cargo ships, large trains, and trucks has ruined habitats and endangered wildlife all over the world. In 1989, the Exxon Valdez dumped 11 million gallons of oil—the volume of about seven school gymnasiums put together—on the Prince William Sound ecosystem in Alaska. Biologists working to clean up the spill question whether or not the site will ever fully recover.

# Engines of Change

In college, I learned about the problems related to burning fossil fuels to power our cars and trucks. I wanted to find an alternative to using fossil fuels to power cars, but what?

When I was studying abroad in Europe my junior year in college, I found it. I was working on a farm in Germany when I noticed that the locals used a yellow liquid—biodiesel—to power their farm equipment. They didn't get their biodiesel from used French fry grease like I do now, though. Biodiesel can be made from any vegetable oil, such as soybean, corn, or sunflower oil. And it works in any kind of diesel engine. In fact, Rudolph Diesel, the inventor of the diesel engine, actually designed his engine to run on biodiesel fuel over 100 years ago.

So how is a car's engine designed to turn the wheels? The car engine is an internal combustion engine, which means fuel is burned inside the engine. Two main types of internal combustion engines are used in automobiles today: gasoline engines and diesel engines. Both engines take advantage of the relationship between temperature, pressure, and volume.

When gases are heated, they expand, taking up more volume. The diagram below shows what would happen if you capped a test tube with a balloon then used a candle to heat the air inside the test tube. As the air's temperature increases, its volume increases.

Say we corked the test tube instead of capping it with a balloon. In this case, the volume of the gas is fixed. When heated, the gas expands, but its volume cannot increase. Instead, the gas pressure increases as the temperature increases.

Temperature, pressure, and volume are related by the following equation, where *P*, *V*, and *T* stand for pressure, volume, and temperature. Because the quantity of air in the engine is a constant, you can use the following relationship to describe how the pressure and temperature are affected by the moving pistons in the combustion chamber:

$$P \; \alpha \; \frac{T}{V}$$

With this in mind, look at the diagram of a diesel engine cylinder below. This type of engine uses a four-stroke combustion cycle to convert the energy in diesel fuel into motion that rotates the engine crankshaft. As the crankshaft rotates, it positions each cylinder to complete an entire combustion cycle. The cycle is described in the following steps:

### Intake Stroke

The piston is positioned at the top of the cylinder, and the intake valve opens. As the piston drops, air is drawn into the cylinder, called the "combustion chamber."

### Compression Stroke

With the piston at the bottom, the intake valve closes and the piston pushes against the air inside of the cylinder, compressing it. As the volume of the chamber decreases, the pressure and temperature of the air inside the chamber increase.

### Power Stroke

At the top of the stroke, fuel is injected into the hot, high-pressure air inside the chamber; it combusts immediately. The combustion spontaneously increases the chamber's pressure and temperature. The expanding gas pushes the piston down with great force. The linear motion of the piston is converted into rotational motion by the crankshaft.

### Exhaust Stroke

As the piston rises a second time, the exhaust valve opens, and the smoke from the explosion exits the engine as exhaust.

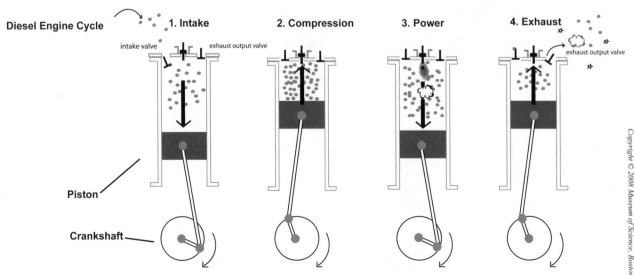

Diesel Engine Cycle

intake valve    exhaust output valve

1. Intake    2. Compression    3. Power    4. Exhaust

exhaust output valve

Piston

Crankshaft

*Engineering the Future: Science, Technology, and the Design Process*

Most car engines use multiple cylinders, which are connected to the crankshaft with connecting rods. The connecting rods are sequenced so that as one piston pushes downward, the turning crankshaft positions the other pistons up or down through a complete combustion cycle. The rapid, repeated cycling of multiple cylinders maintains the rotational motion of the crankshaft, which rotates the vehicle's wheels.

## Gasoline versus Diesel

Diesel and gasoline engines have a few differences. One main difference is how the fuel-air mixture is ignited. As described above, a diesel engine compresses air, which raises its temperature and pressure. The engine injects fuel into the hot, high-pressure air, causing it to ignite. Gasoline engines, on the other hand, use spark plugs to ignite the pressurized fuel-air mixture in the cylinder. In this country, diesel engines power trains, large trucks, cargo ships, bulldozers, buses, and other heavy-duty vehicles because the engines can move the wheels of these heavier vehicles with greater force than a gasoline engine can. Gasoline engines won't run on diesel fuel or biodiesel, so don't try putting biodiesel in a gasoline engine!

Why do most American cars have gasoline engines? For one reason, diesel engines are hard to start in cold climates. And, historically, diesel engine exhaust has contained more soot and other pollutants than gasoline engine exhaust. Have you ever stood behind an idling bus or truck? If so, then you know that the fumes the vehicle emits have a strong, smoky smell. This exhaust arises from the incomplete combustion of the diesel fuel in the chamber. Soot blackens buildings and irritates people's lungs. States with pollution problems have taken measures to curb the number of diesel-powered vehicles on their roads. In recent years, California has placed limits on the sale and use of diesel vehicles.

Biodiesel works in a diesel engine the same way that diesel fuel does, but it doesn't produce nearly as much toxic soot. Recent life cycle analysis of biodiesel fuel made from the seeds of rape plants has found that biodiesel does not contribute to global warming. Yes, carbon gases are released to the atmosphere during the combustion of biodiesel, but biodiesel is a made from plants. When plants grow, they "breathe" in carbon dioxide and expel oxygen during photosynthesis. The plant essentially removes carbon from the atmosphere and uses it to grow.

The burning of 1,000 gallons of biodiesel fuel will release exactly as much carbon as one acre of plants will absorb from the atmosphere. As long as new crops are replanted after others have been harvested to make oil, the total amount of carbon in the atmosphere will not increase.

The Veggie Van

## Where the Rubber Meets the Road

Doesn't biodiesel sound like a great solution? I thought so too! And I wanted to communicate my solution to the world. So I decided to drive across the country to promote biodiesel.

I bought a small diesel-powered camper van. My friends and I repainted it with wild, colorful pictures to make it highly visible. When people see my "Veggie Van," they can't miss it! I also built a special trailer to haul the equipment needed to convert waste cooking oil into useful biodiesel fuel. We named the trailer the "Green Grease Machine," and filled it with pumps, filters, vats, and all the equipment we needed to make the fuel. With this equipment, we could park behind McDonald's, pump out the waste cooking grease, put it through the Green Grease Machine, pour it into the Veggie Van's fuel tank, and drive away.

I'll never forget the first time I made my own biodiesel fuel using the Green Grease Machine. I drove around Sarasota collecting used oil from fast-food restaurants. Then some friends and I mixed the oil with alcohol and added a pinch of lye, a substance used to make soap. We stirred a large vat of the mixture using an old boat motor and let it sit over night. The next morning, we poured the concoction into the Veggie Van and hit the ignition. Did the homemade biodiesel power the Veggie Van? You bet it did! We've driven the Veggie Van across America twice, powered by old cooking grease!

People who follow the Veggie Van on the highway say the exhaust smells like French fries. (Is that why I'm always hungry?) Fast food gives me energy and the waste cooking grease gives the Veggie Van energy. If I have my way, more and more people will start using plant oil to fuel their cars. As I said before, about 1,000 gallons of useful vegetable oil can be produced from the plants grown on one acre of land every year. That's enough fuel to power a car for about 2,000 miles! And plants are a renewable resource, meaning we can grow them year after year. Fossil fuels, on the other hand, are non-renewable, meaning they won't replenish themselves.

One of my favorite things about biodiesel is that we can grow it right here on American soil. We don't have to buy it from other nations. Powering your car with biodiesel supports American farmers and boosts our national economy.

Because of the environmental and health effects of fossil fuels, I believe we must find cleaner sources of energy. My Veggie Van project is proof that it just takes a bit of thought to find solutions to the very serious energy challenges we face today. These solutions aren't always brand-new technologies. Biodiesel has powered engines for over a century. When it comes to finding a new way to fuel our cars, we may need to look no further than the frying pan.

Josh with his book, *Biodiesel America*

##  What's the Story?

1.  What's the difference between a gas engine and diesel engine?

2   Give both an advantage and a disadvantage of a diesel engine over a gasoline engine.

## Designing with Math and Science

3.  What is the relationship between volume, temperature, and pressure that is useful for designing things with fixed-volume pistons?

4.  What information would you need to know to determine the force with which the piston pushes the air during the second step of the diesel cycle? (Remember: the formula for pressure is in Chapter 17.)

5.  What will happen to the pressure of the gas in the chamber as the volume of gas in the chamber expands in the third step?

## Connecting the Dots

6.  Whenever energy is transferred, some energy is always transferred to the environment. Where might a diesel engine transfer some energy to the environment?

## What Do You Think?

7.  Other engineers have tackled the problem of making more efficient cars. What are some new car technologies in development today that are designed to reduce the use of fossil fuels?

# 20

# *An Ingenious Engine*

## Chris Langenfeld

Courtesy of Chris Langenfeld

### Key Concepts
#### from Previous Chapters

15 Energy Transfer and Storage

17 Working Fluid

19 Internal Combustion System

A few years ago, my boss had a vision to create a better wheelchair. After many years and countless prototypes, we finally landed on a great design. The IBOT™ Mobility System, sold by Johnson & Johnson, can climb stairs and balance on its two back wheels to lift the occupant to standing height. We designed the wheelchair with four rear wheels instead of two, so it's kind of like a truck. The extra wheels make it stable but also give it tremendous balance and climbing capability. This design gives users remarkable freedom, helping to restore independence to people who've suffered loss of physical mobility.

This kind of project gives me a lot of satisfaction. I'm Chris Langenfeld, and I'm an engineering manager at Deka Research, a design firm based in Manchester, New Hampshire. Our firm creates new products and technologies that help people.

The IBOT Mobility System

Courtesy of Chris Langenfeld, Deka Research and Development Corporation

We do research and development for other companies. In other words, we design new products, and then we submit our designs to other companies who manufacture and sell them.

In my opinion, Deka is about the greatest place on Earth to work. Our founder and my boss, Dean Kamen, is a famous inventor who holds over 150 patents for new devices, many of them medical technologies. He firmly believes in the virtues of technology and has made it his mission to educate the world about them. His enthusiasm is contagious. Since I've worked here, I've seen for myself just how much well-designed technologies can improve people's lives.

## A Closed-System Engine

Just after we started our wheelchair project, we realized that our design would need a lot of power to make it run. At the time, the best battery available was the ordinary lead-acid storage battery, much like what's used in a car. But because our wheelchair had multiple motors for the wheels and electronics for control and balance, we needed more power than a lead-acid storage battery could supply. Our wheelchair needed an engine.

But what kind of engine would work? We knew that the right engine for our wheelchair had to be quiet. Internal combustion engines make a lot of noise when the fuel combusts in the cylinders. Then we remembered a tiny, very quiet engine invented long ago, the Stirling engine.

Robert Stirling, a Scottish minister, invented the Stirling engine in 1816. Stirling designed his engine to be a *closed system*—that is, the working fluid stays inside the engine instead of passing through it, as happens in a car engine. The term "working fluid" refers to the fluid—usually a gas—that actually moves inside an engine. In a closed-system engine, only energy moves across the system boundary.

Stirling's design was, and still is, a marvel of technology. The engine works by heating and cooling the working fluid. As you recall, gases expand when heated and contract when cooled. If the gas is in a flexible container, the volume of the container will increase or decrease depending on the change in the gas's temperature.

In a *closed system,* the working fluid remains within the system.

In an *open system,* the working fluid moves across the system boundary.

If you were to look inside one type of Stirling engine, you would see something like the diagram below. A large cylinder full of the working fluid has a displacer in it that can rise and fall easily. At the top of the cylinder, there is a piston, called the "power piston." The displacer and the power piston are both connected to a crankshaft in such a way that when the power piston rises to maximum height, the displacer piston is nudged down. The up and down movement of the piston turns the crankshaft, which spins a flywheel.

Robert Stirling
(1790–1878)

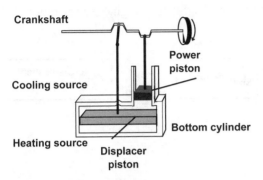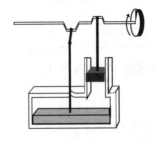

1. The bottom cylinder is heated. The displacer piston is pushed up.

2. The power piston is pushed up, which causes the crankshaft to turn.

The bottom of the cylinder is heated to start the engine. The working fluid expands, increasing the pressure underneath the displacer piston and pushing the piston up. As the displacer rises, the working fluid at the top of the chamber pushes the power piston up. The power piston pushes on the crankshaft, causing it to turn. When the power piston reaches the top of its stroke, the crankshaft nudges the displacer down. Fluid flows around the displacer to the top of the cylinder, where the gas is cooled by ice or cold water. As the gas is cooled, the pressure in the cylinder decreases and the displacer piston falls. At the bottom of the piston's stroke, the crankshaft nudges the displacer up. Fluid flows around the displacer to the bottom of the cylinder, where it is heated, and the cycle begins again. If you were to diagram how the energy moves through the system, you'd see that it flows from the energy source through the engine to the spinning crankshaft. Any energy that is not transferred to the spinning crankshaft is transferred to the cooling "source." The cooling "source" is not really a source at all. It's an object with lower temperature (less energy) than the heat source. Energy always flows from the higher-energy object to the lower-energy object. In fact, it may be more appropriate to refer to the cooling "source" as a "heat sink."

The greater the temperature difference between the top and bottom of the engine, the greater the amount of energy transferred to move the pistons and spin the flywheel. The energy source could be anything hot—burning fossil fuel, wood, or dry sugar cane, hot water from a solar collector, or steam from a geothermal well. Likewise, the heat sink could be any lower-temperature object—water, ice, even a cool breeze. In a Stirling engine, the working gas never leaves the engine the way it does in an internal combustion engine. There are no explosions, and there are no exhaust valves. The Stirling engine is very quiet.

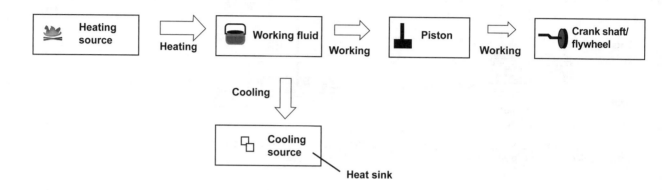

Our plan for the wheelchair was to use a small propane tank as a fuel source to heat up one side of the Stirling engine. Water is used as the heat sink. Propane gas cylinders are cheap and they're available at most hardware stores or home centers.

While it's possible to use room air as the working fluid, a Stirling engine works much better with helium gas. Helium transfers energy very effectively. But helium tends to escape easily from containers. Our engineering team put the Stirling engine inside another sealed container filled with helium. And, of course, we have small pipes that allow us to circulate hot gasses from the burning propane around the "hot" side, and a cold liquid, such as cold water, around the "cold" side. The high-pressure working fluid stays safely sealed inside, and the engine can run for years and years without worry.

Now we had an excellent power source for the wheelchair. During the time it took to develop the wheelchair and the generating engine, however, battery technology improved radically. In a few short years, batteries became so improved that we decided to develop the IBOT using the new type of batteries instead of our power-generating engine. We put our engine on the shelf for a while.

Recently, we've discovered some great alternative uses for our engine. We're working on a water purification system that can provide clean drinking water for a few families or a small village. Our vision is to use this purification system in poor, third-world countries where babies and children become sick and die every day from polluted water. The Deka purification system would be a small-scale machine that, hopefully, we can make available to millions of people who have never had clean water for safe cooking and washing.

We're also looking into the possibility that our generator could provide supplemental power in the big diesel trucks that drive coast to coast. Often the drivers stop for the night and stay in their sleeper cabs. They allow their diesel engines to idle all night to provide power for their TVs, microwaves, air conditioners, heaters, and so on. But these diesel engines pollute, particularly when idling. We envision that our Stirling engine could run on a much smaller amount of fuel to provide the electrical power the truckers need for their sleeper cabs.

In my view, the Stirling engine offers society advantages for producing electricity in an environmentally friendly way, particularly when it draws energy from the sun or geothermal wells. And whether run by external combustion, such as burning wood, or pollution-free sources, such as solar or geothermal energy, the Stirling engine can generate electricity reliably, cleanly, and quietly. I always find it amazing how technologies invented long ago can, with a few improvements, suit our modern needs very well. The best designs are truly timeless. I often wonder if, one hundred years from now, people will still use the IBOT or some other technology that I helped to develop. Regardless, I have complete faith that the work we are doing today at Deka will influence inventors of the future. That's how it is in engineering. In the same way that scientific knowledge accumulates over time, each new technology builds on the ones that came before it—and every engineer draws inspiration from his or her predecessors.

## What's the Story?

1. Why is the Stirling engine considered a closed system?

2. What were the design requirements for the wheelchair engine? Why did the Stirling engine seem like it might meet the criteria?

3. Why wasn't the engine that Chris's team redesigned used in the wheelchair? How might it be used?

## Designing with Math and Science

4. Chris describes the "cooling source" as an "energy sink." Why is the term "energy sink" more appropriate?

5. Chris says that the greater the temperature difference between the top and bottom of the Stirling engine, the greater the amount of energy transferred to move the pistons and spin the flywheel. Explain.

## Connecting the Dots

6. In a Stirling engine, the working gas never leaves the engine. Describe how this is different than a combustion engine.

7. Given what you know about renewable energy sources, explain how the Stirling engine may be used in a way that is beneficial to the environment.

## What Do You Think?

8. If you were to manually turn the crankshaft of a Stirling engine, the engine would work in reverse. It would pump energy from one side of the engine to the other. Over time, one side of the engine would become cool and the other side hot. What might be some practical applications of this?

9. Be creative and think of a way that a closed-system engine like the Stirling engine might be applied.

*Engineering the Future: Science, Technology, and the Design Process*

# 21

# *Energy from the Earth*

## Ron DiPippo

### Key Concepts
#### from Previous Chapters

- 15 Temperature
- 15 Differences Drive Change
- 15 Energy Transfer and Storage
- 16 Efficiency
- 17 Pressure
- 19 Engines

I'll never forget the day I learned about an energy source that would change the way I think about energy and power. I was in the library browsing through some magazines, when I happened to see an article about geothermal energy. "Free power with no pollution!" the article proclaimed. This was a radical idea. In a world where we pay a big price for power—in both outright costs and environmental degradation—could we really get electrical power for free? And without pollution? I couldn't imagine it.

My name is Ron DiPippo, and I recently retired as a professor of engineering at the University of Massachusetts at Dartmouth. It wasn't until I was well along in my teaching career—about twenty-five years ago—that I saw the article about geothermal energy. I was intrigued enough to do more research into geothermal energy.

I learned that geothermal power plants could replace some conventional electrical power plants, which burn fossil fuels, in certain locations. I also learned that geothermal plants could generate electricity more cheaply while producing far less air pollution then conventional plants.

You can understand why finding cleaner and cheaper power options is so important if you consider just how many of our technologies require electricity to work. Think of all the electrical devices you encounter during a typical day: streetlights, computers, televisions, telephones, and cell phones, to name a few. Our designed world is full of them! There's no indication that Americans will be using less electrical power in the near future. Therefore, I think it's critical that we find cost-effective and environmentally friendly ways to produce electrical power. Geothermal power is both cleaner and cheaper. That's why I've spent the last two decades traveling the world to help engineers build geothermal power plants.

## The Basics

Where does electricity come from? Right now, we generate most of our electricity by burning fossil fuels—natural gas, coal, or oil—to heat water. The water boils and turns into steam. This steam is then used to spin a steam turbine. The spinning of the turbine drives a generator, which creates electricity.

Burning fossil fuels to generate electricity leads to some serious environmental and health problems. Geothermal power plants eliminate the need for burning fossil fuels altogether. A geothermal power plant uses steam and hot water from geothermal wells. These geothermal wells form when pools of water under molten rocks deep below the Earth's surface are heated up. The water boils, creating steam. The large increase in volume increases the pressure in the well, and the pressure difference between the well and the atmosphere gets big enough that the hot steam and water erupt from the Earth's surface as a geyser. It's a ready-made energy source for a geothermal power plant!

How does hot steam cause a turbine to spin? This subject is one I know and love. I've been a professor of thermodynamics, which is the study of heating and working. In a steam engine, water is heated into steam, the gas form of water. When water boils into steam, its volume increases by as much as 1,600 times.

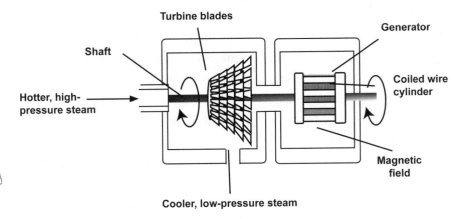

The hot, high-pressure steam enters one end of a chamber, creating a difference in the chamber. Which way will the energy and matter tend to flow? That's right, from the area of higher concentration to the area of lower concentration. The steam expands and moves through the chamber to the exit. As the steam's volume increases, its temperature and pressure decrease, creating a temperature change, or gradient. When more hot steam enters the chamber, it will flow from the hotter side to the cooler side, creating convection current as it moves. **Convection** is energy transfer due to fluid motion.

**Convection** is an energy transfer due to fluid motion.

As it travels, the convection current hits the angled blades of a turbine. A turbine is like a huge fan with a long series of angled blades. When the moving fluid hits the turbine, the turbine spins much like a pinwheel spins when you blow on it. As the steam transfers its energy to the blades, causing the blades to turn, the steam loses energy, becoming cooler. The turning blades drive a generator that produces electricity. (You'll learn just how a generator produces electricity in Unit 4.) The energy flows through miles of electrical wiring to businesses and residences where you and I can use it simply by plugging in an appliance or flipping a light switch.

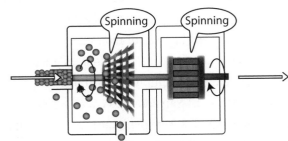

Steam transfers energy to blades, causing them to turn. Steam loses energy and becomes cooler. The turning blades cause the generator to produce electricity.

## The Benefits of Geothermal

Geothermal energy is what's called a renewable energy source. A **renewable energy source** is an energy source that is naturally replenished in a short time. As soon as water flows back over the molten rocks in the underground well, the cycle begins again. Some of the folks who first discovered this use for geothermal wells back in the 1960s worked for oil companies. These companies were drilling in the Imperial Valley in Southern California. Occasionally they would hit large underground reserves of water and steam instead of oil. One day, a few oil company executives had a thought: We burn oil or coal to make steam, and then use the steam to drive generators that make electricity. Why not make electricity with the steam directly from these wells and skip burning the oil or coal? It was a very good question, one that led to the development of geothermal technologies.

No power plant can ever be 100 percent efficient. The useful energy outputs will never equal energy inputs because some energy is "lost" to the environment every time energy is transferred. In a typical power plant, the input is coal, oil, or natural gas, and the output is electricity. In a plant that is 100 percent efficient, the electricity leaving the plant should carry the same amount of energy as the coal that is burned. In reality, however, the coal-burning power plants are only about 35 percent efficient.

Where is all of the "lost" energy? Some energy is lost to the air when the coal is burned. A little more energy is lost in the second transfer when the convection currents turn the turbine—some of the energy of the hot steam never gets transferred to the turning blades and instead heats up the chamber.

More energy is lost in the third and final transfer, when the spinning turbine turns the generator. Other losses occur as well. Creating electricity from geothermal energy sources eliminates all the losses associated with the combustion processes. Geothermal power plants tend to be more efficient than typical fossil fuel power plants, having an average efficiency of about 40 to 45 percent.

A few logistical challenges arise when it's time to build the plant. Geothermal power plants need a very large and constant supply of steam so enough energy is available to operate the electricity and account for inefficiency. The large reserves of hot steam exist underground in many places on Earth, but they can be hard to access. Some countries are well-known for their many sources of geothermal energy. In fact, in some places, these geothermal sources are under so much pressure that the hot water and steam simply shoot above the ground.

One such place is located in El Salvador. It's called *Agua Shuca,* which means "dirty water" in Spanish. It was a small, quiet hot spring that people from nearby villages used for washing their clothes. On October 13, 1990, during the night while all the villagers were asleep, Agua Shuca erupted without warning,

A **renewable energy** source is an energy source that is naturally replenished in a short amount of time.

*Engineering the Future: Science, Technology, and the Design Process*

as geothermal sites are known to do. Hot water and mud, boulders, and steam rushed skyward with a tremendous blast. Some people were killed instantly and others were injured. What had been a 10-foot diameter pool of boiling water was turned into a 100-foot-wide by 50-foot-deep crater with vents of mud, hot water, and steam.

A few months after the eruption, I was asked to visit the area and make recommendations about building a geothermal power plant there. When I saw the village, only a few huts remained. Mud could be seen stuck high in the branches of the trees near the springs.

The tremendous energy stored in geothermal wells is apparent in situations like this one. We can use that energy, but we also must take precautions. I always encourage geothermal engineers to design many safety features into their wells, piping, and power plants. You just never know when Mother Nature will lose her temper.

Here I am consulting at a well site in Costa Rica.

In Central America, large geothermal sites are commonplace. El Salvador produces almost 25 percent of its electricity with geothermal power plants. Guatemala, Nicaragua, and Costa Rica also draw a substantial portion of their power from geothermal plants.

I've helped engineers in Kenya, Costa Rica, El Salvador, Guatemala and other nations develop geothermal resources. Geothermal wells are expensive to build, costing as much as $1 million per well. You can never know for sure that you will find hot water until you drill a well. But because of the high cost of drilling, you should have a good idea that you will. I help engineers to decide where to drill wells based on proximity to other geothermal sites. After the well is drilled and the amount of hot water is determined, I make recommendations about how to build a power plant around it.

One type of plant I designed with some students actually uses both fossil fuel and geothermal energy to make electricity. In this type of plant, a combination of coal or natural gas and geothermal energy is used to heat water to create steam for the turbine. This system is necessary when the water from a geothermal source is not hot enough or runs in too short a supply to create enough electricity on its own. The system is more efficient than regular fossil fuel plants. So, while some pollution results from the burning of fossil fuels, the amount is greatly reduced because we burn less coal or gas to get the same amount of electricity that we would in a conventional power plant.

When I started working with engineers in Costa Rica in 1994, the country had only three geothermal wells. Now scores of wells and four geothermal power plants produce electricity in an environmentally clean manner. Overall, in 2001, about 10 percent of Central America's electrical power came from geothermal energy.

## Geothermal in the United States

While we don't have many large geothermal sites in the United States, we do have a few. You probably know about Old Faithful in Yellowstone National Park. Every sixty to ninety minutes, Old Faithful erupts, shooting hot water and steam 100–200 feet into the air. But it does this for only several minutes. While it's a spectacular sight, it would be very impractical for geothermal power. Why? The geothermal energy would be available for only a few minutes every hour or so. We could never rely on a generator with such a sporadic schedule.

The first geothermal plants in the United States were almost a disaster. Engineers quickly discovered that the hot water and steam from deep in the Earth was full of contaminants. In some places, the hot water has ten times the level of salt that we find in seawater. Why? Because when you increase the temperature of water, you can dissolve more in it. Think of how instant hot chocolate powder dissolves faster in hot water than in cold water. The hot water below the surface—400 or 500 degrees Fahrenheit in some places—can dissolve all kinds of minerals, salts, and even metals. When this watery mixture reaches the surface, the pressure and temperature drop, and all of that dissolved stuff emerges as solids. In some places, early geothermal experiments were plagued by clogged pipes—they would plug with minerals within just a day or two.

Chemical and civil engineers who worked on waste treatment plants devised ways to filter out the contaminants so they wouldn't clog the power generators. And do you know what they found? Zinc, silver, even gold! The "junk" that was clogging the pipes was actually loaded with valuable minerals and metals. These geothermal wells delivered much more to the surface than hot water!

Another problem with geothermal energy is water availability. Remember that Old Faithful erupts only every ninety minutes or so because only a trickle of water seeps through the ground to refill it. When enough water has dribbled in, it boils. The pressure increase in the well causes water and steam to blast to the surface. As soon as it blasts into the air, the source is depleted until more water collects.

Courtesy of PDPhoto.org

Old Faithful Geyser

*Engineering the Future: Science, Technology, and the Design Process*

Engineers working with the first geothermal power plants noticed something similar. When they first started the power plants, plenty of hot water and steam was available to spin the turbines and generate electricity. But as the plants used the hot water and steam, the amount reaching the surface steadily decreased. Just like Old Faithful, the output of the geothermal well was limited by the recharge rate—or the rate at which fresh water would flow underground back over the hot rock. In these cases, engineers were taking the water out, but not putting any water back in. If too little water were flowing over the hot magma, then too little hot water would come up the wells. And the more water they took out, the less remained to come up. What to do?

Towns near some well fields in California had another problem: finding the best way to dispose of excess wastewater from their sewage treatment plants. While the water was partially cleaned, it was not suitable for domestic use. It also could not be discharged into rivers and lakes, so it had to be disposed of in other ways. The engineers devised a means to pump this unwanted "gray water" into the geothermal wells. Eureka! Two problems solved at once. The contaminated wastewater was sent down into the hot geothermal wells, where the very high-temperature rocks energized it. The pressurized steam came up through the geothermal well, bringing energy with it.

It just goes to show you that with some creativity, solutions are possible for even the most dumbfounding problems. I truly believe that solving the problems associated with fossil fuels will be an engineering task more challenging and complex than going to the moon was in the 1960s. But the energy we need is all around us. Sure, we must be extraordinarily clever to figure out how to harness the energy. But a little ingenuity goes a long way!

Northern California is well known for its geothermal resources. Most of the United State's geothermal power plants are located there.

Navy 1 Geothermal Power Plants in Coso Junction, CA

The Leathers Geothermal Power Plant in Calipatria, CA

## What's the Story?

1. Why are there so few geothermal power plants in the United States?

2. According to Ron, what are some of the benefits of geothermal power plants?

3. What's the basic difference between fossil fuel–burning power plants and geothermal power plants?

## Designing with Math and Science

4. What is convection?

5. Why is convection critical to the function of a steam turbine?

6. Why are geothermal power plants usually more efficient than fossil fuel–burning power plants?

## Connecting the Dots

7. Ron mentions that geothermal energy is a renewable energy source. What other renewable energy sources have you learned about in this book?

## What Do You Think?

8. Imagine that you have been asked to design your own power plant with an unlimited budget. Use your imagination to brainstorm some other ways you could make a turbine spin to generate electricity without burning a fossil fuel.

# Good Chemistry

## Dr. Rebecca Steinmann

Courtesy of Rebecca Steinmann

### Key Concepts
#### from Previous Chapters

While engineers are often involved with designing or improving new technologies, that's not all they do. Many engineers make sure that existing designed systems are safe, reliable, and well maintained. This job is especially important when the designed system in question is as large and complex as a nuclear power plant. Nuclear power plants provide approximately 20 percent of the United States's electrical power. More than 100 nuclear power plants operate in the United States, and each plant must meet stringent federal regulations. These regulations help ensure the plants are safe for the people who work in them, the people who live nearby, and the environment.

I'm Dr. Rebecca Steinman, and I'm a nuclear engineer working at Advent Engineering Services, Inc., a small engineering consulting company based in Ann Arbor, Michigan. As a consultant, I'm often involved in helping nuclear power plants meet federal regulations.

I decided I wanted to become a nuclear engineer when I was a junior in high school. I entered a local science fair that year—and won. The state contest was held at the University of Missouri at Rolla campus, which had a research nuclear reactor. I got to go into the control room! I was fascinated by the fact that the energy released from nuclear reactions is invisible, but we can do so much with it. We use it to generate electrical power, for sterilization, and for medical diagnosis and treatment, along with many other applications.

When I got home from the science fair, I announced to my grandmother and her bridge partners that I planned to become a nuclear engineer. As I expected, they all gasped in disbelief. At the time, very few women worked in engineering and even fewer worked in nuclear engineering. My desire to become a nuclear engineer was really shocking to some people, and I must admit that I sort of enjoyed challenging stereotypes about who should study engineering. I was the only woman out of eighteen nuclear engineering majors in my graduating class at the University of Missouri. Since graduating, I have completed my Ph.D. in nuclear engineering and have worked in the field for several years. Over those years, I have seen the field start to change. Nuclear engineering programs are attracting a more diverse group of students today. I'm glad to see this change happen. I believe nuclear engineering offers many opportunities for anyone who chooses to enter the profession.

## The Basics of Nuclear Power Plants

Because I work for a consulting company, I get to work on a variety of different projects, sometimes in teams and sometimes on my own. But nearly all of my assignments involve nuclear power plants.

Much like coal-fired power plants or geothermal power plants, nuclear power plants use hot water or steam to turn a turbine, which spins an electrical generator. The primary difference between these three types of power plants is how the water is heated. In a coal-fired plant, the water is heated by a chemical reaction. A geothermal power plant uses water heated deep in the Earth. A nuclear power plant uses the energy released by nuclear reactions to heat water and drive a turbine.

# How Do Nuclear Reactors Work?

To understand how nuclear reactions heat water, it's important to remember that all substances on Earth are made up of molecules. A *molecule* is the smallest particle of a material that has all the chemical properties of that material. Molecules are made up of even smaller particles called *atoms.* A water molecule, for example, has two hydrogen atoms and one oxygen atom, which is abbreviated $H_2O$.

**$H_2O$ molecule:**
2 Hydrogen atoms
1 Oxygen atoms

Substances that have only one kind of atom are called *elements.* Most molecules of oxygen in our air are made up of two atoms of oxygen ($O_2$). Other substances in the form of a gas at room temperature include hydrogen, helium, neon, and nitrogen. Elements in solid form at room temperature include iron, gold, silver, carbon, and uranium. There are ninety-two natural elements in all.

In *chemical reactions,* molecules break apart and the atoms are rearranged into new molecules. When molecules break apart, they release energy, usually as heat and light. When a carbon-based fuel like gasoline burns, for example, the carbon (C) is released from the gasoline molecules and energy is released to the immediate surroundings. The carbon then combines with oxygen from the air (O), forming carbon dioxide gas ($CO_2$).

$$C + O_2 \longrightarrow = CO_2$$

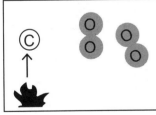

Burning fuel releases carbon (C) into the air.

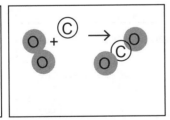

Carbon combines with oxygen in air ($O_2$), forming carbon dioxide gas ($CO_2$).

**Elements**
are substances that have only one kind of atom.

**Atoms**
are the smallest particle of a chemical element that retains its chemical properties.

**A molecule**
is the smallest particle of a material that still has all the chemical properties of that material. Usually a molecule has two or more atoms.

**In chemical reactions**
molecules break apart and atoms are rearranged into new molecules.

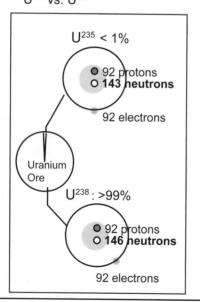

Helium    Hydrogen    Nucleus

Proton    Neutron    Electron

In **nuclear reactions,** the atoms themselves—not the molecules—break up. This process releases much more energy. The action happens in the center of each atom, where there is a tiny, dense ball of matter called the **nucleus.** The nucleus consists of two types of particles: **protons** and **neutrons.**

The number of protons determines the kind of element. All hydrogen atoms have one proton in the nucleus, while all helium atoms have two protons. Uranium atoms are the heaviest atoms in nature, with ninety-two protons. Atoms of a given element often have the same number of neutrons in their nucleus, or a few more or less.

The element **uranium** is especially interesting to nuclear engineers, because it can be used as a remarkably efficient fuel. A pound of the type of uranium used in nuclear power plants, roughly the size of a tennis ball, can release about as much energy as one million gallons of gasoline.

Uranium occurs naturally, often in the form of an ore. This ore is slightly radioactive, which means that some of the atoms in the rock naturally decay, releasing energy in the form of heat and particles as they come apart. More than 99 percent of the uranium in ore is $U^{238}$, which means it has ninety-two protons for a total of 238 particles in its nucleus. Although $U^{238}$ is not radioactive enough to use in a nuclear reactor, it does contain trace amounts (less than 1 percent) of a different form of uranium, $U^{235}$, which is much more potent. The uranium atom used in nuclear fuel has 92 protons and 143 neutrons, for a total of 235 particles in its nucleus. This form of uranium is symbolized $U^{235}$. One of the first steps in producing or supplying a nuclear reactor is to isolate $U^{235}$ from the much more abundant $U^{238}$.

Uranium

Atomic number

92

U    Symbol

Uranium
238.02891    Atomic weight

$U^{238}$ vs. $U^{235}$

$U^{235}$ < 1%

92 protons
143 neutrons

92 electrons

Uranium
Ore

$U^{238}$ : >99%

92 protons
146 neutrons

92 electrons

- $U^{238}$ is not radioactive enough to use in a nuclear reactor.
- $U^{235}$ is much more potent than, but not as abundant as, $U^{238}$.
- $U^{235}$ needs to be isolated from $U^{238}$.
- Nuclear reactors need $U^{235}$.

Inside a nuclear reactor are thousands of nuclear fuel pellets made of $U_{235}$. When a neutron wanders by, it will be "captured" and form a slightly larger nucleus. This larger nucleus cannot hold together very long, so it splits into two smaller nuclei, releasing energy. This splitting of the nucleus is called nuclear *fission.*

When it splits, the uranium nucleus also emits two or three more neutrons, each of which can be captured by two or three other uranium nuclei. These nuclei also emit energy and each releases more neutrons, which are captured by more nuclei and so on. This is called a chain reaction. If enough uranium exists in one place and the reaction continues unchecked, the result would be a nuclear explosion. However, in a power reactor, control rods are used to absorb some of the neutrons. The splitting of the nuclei of uranium atoms generates heat, which heats water in a boiler creating steam.

Nuclear reactors come in many different designs. Each reactor is designed to be as efficient and safe as possible. Most reactors in the United States are "Pressurized Water Reactors." In this kind of reactor, the uranium fuel is made into ceramic pellets about the size of a fingertip. Hundreds of these pellets are sealed in strong metal tubes and inserted into a pool of water. Control rods are also dispersed in the water, between the tubes of uranium pellets. This assembly is called the reactor core. Fission begins when enough uranium is inserted into the core to maintain a chain reaction. By controlling the position of the control rods, operators can keep the chain reaction going at a constant rate.

As the fission reaction continues, the water in the reactor becomes very hot. However, it is kept under pressure so it does not turn to steam. The hot water is then used to heat a second tank of water called a boiler. When water in the second tank is heated, it turns into steam. The steam drives a turbine, which spins an electrical generator. The hot water in the second tank is then cooled in a cooling tower and is recycled or discarded.

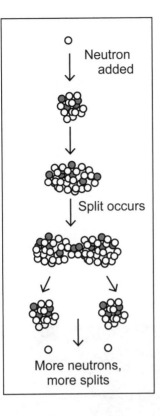

# Nuclear Power: Perceptions and Facts

Nuclear power plants have some important advantages over fossil fuel power plants. Because they do not require combustion, nuclear power plants do not release air pollution. And they do not use oil, which is a diminishing natural resource. Because of these advantages, the federal government has recently invested in national and international efforts to boost nuclear power production to help meet the world's rapidly growing electrical power needs in a more environmentally friendly way.

While nuclear power generation is a cleaner alternative to fossil fuel power generation in terms of air pollution, nuclear power has some risks associated with it. Nuclear power plants use radioactive materials, such as uranium, which emit radiation. High levels of radiation can damage or destroy cells of living organisms, potentially leading to cell mutation or cancer. This risk explains why there are so many laws regulating the nuclear power industry.

*Courtesy of Morguefile*

In nuclear power plants that meet federal regulation, however, the risks are very, very minimal. Well-constructed and well-managed plants release very little radiation into the environment. In fact, coal-fired power plants often emit more radiation than nuclear power plants do because radioactive materials naturally occurring in coal are released during the combustion process.

Even though the safety record of nuclear power plants in the United States is very good, nuclear power remains a controversial means of producing power in our country. Many people perceive nuclear power plants as dangerous. The perception may stem, in part, from an accident that occurred in 1979 at the Three Mile Island nuclear power station near Harrisburg, Pennsylvania. It was the worst accident in U.S. commercial reactor history. During the accident, coolant escaped from the reactor due to a mechanical malfunction and human error.

No one was injured, and no overexposure to radiation resulted. But major media outlets across the nation greatly publicized the story. Public demand for stricter plant regulation soon followed. Later that year, the United States Nuclear Regulatory Commission (NRC) imposed stricter reactor safety regulations and more rigid inspection procedures to improve the safety of reactor operations. The NRC continues to create regulations and industry standards, enforce laws, and license and certify all U.S. nuclear power plants. As a part of this mandate, the NRC has developed the environmental qualification process.

# Environmental Qualification

Numerous processes and programs have been established to ensure that all nuclear plant equipment will function as expected under normal and possible accidental conditions. Environmental qualification is a process for ensuring that all of the plant's electrical equipment will function properly, even during the extreme temperatures and pressures that could exist in the event of an accident at the plant. All nuclear power plants in this country must undergo this process to receive a license to operate. As a consultant, I am often involved in conducting tests to certify a plant's environmental qualification.

During the initial environmental qualification of the plant's electrical equipment, my team double-checks that every safety-related piece of electrical equipment (including sensors, wiring, connectors, and so on) has passed rigorous tests. Then, over the life of the plant, we ensure the equipment is maintained and operated in a manner that ensures that it will function as expected in an accident.

The diversity and quantity of equipment requires that a team consist of many different skill sets. Electrical engineers confirm that the plant's electrical wiring is updated and functioning well. Mechanical engineers ensure that the plant's environments are suitable for equipment and personnel. Structural engineers make sure the plant is structurally sound and that the equipment is properly protected from accidental damage.

In addition to environmental qualification, a plant must meet hundreds of pages of federal safety regulations. These regulations extend to the employees as well. Every employee of a plant must be extensively trained in operations and safety procedures. Employees must take measures to reduce exposure to radiation, such as wearing protective clothing or gear.

As a nuclear engineer, I also help power plants develop emergency procedures. According to law, every nuclear plant must have evacuation plans. Plants are required to develop an evacuation plan for an area within a ten-mile radius of the plant, and another plan for an area within a fifty-mile radius of the plant. Designing an evacuation plan can be very complex. If a plant is located near a city, or an area where the population does not have access to transportation, we must prove that systems are in place for moving all of those people out of the evacuation zone quickly and safely.

## Processing Spent Fuel

I've also designed systems for the safe transportation of any spent nuclear fuel left over from the fission process. Even though a lot of energy is extracted in a reactor, the spent nuclear fuel is still radioactive and will remain so for hundreds of years. Therefore, it must be handled carefully. Power plants store much of their spent fuel in large pools of water on the power plant grounds. But many plants are running out of room for spent fuel and must start considering other storage options.

Currently, the federal government is planning to build a large repository for spent fuel in the Yucca Mountain in Nevada. To get the spent fuel to Yucca Mountain for storage, power plant operators will need to ship it by truck or train. Obviously, if a train or truck carrying radioactive materials were to have an accident, there would be a risk of releasing radioactive materials into the environment. To prevent such an accident, strong casks must be used to ship spent fuel. These casks can withstand high forces without breaking, and I mean very high forces! To test the casks thoroughly, researchers drive trains into them and even drop them from helicopters. Of course, even a very strong cask could break if it experiences high enough forces during a collision. Breakage is unlikely, but just in case, it's necessary to plan routes that will allow vehicles carrying radioactive materials to avoid areas with large populations, agricultural areas, or water supplies as much as possible. This strategy means damage would be minimized in the event of an accident and a cracked cask.

Nuclear power has great potential to help our nation meet its energy needs. But, as with any designed system that involves the use of hazardous materials, nuclear power plants must be maintained and updated continuously to keep them as safe as possible.

## What's the Story?

1. What are the benefits of nuclear power plants?

2. List three ways that engineers ensure the safety of nuclear power plants.

## Designing with Math and Science

3. What is the difference between a chemical reaction and a nuclear reaction? When coal is burned, is it a chemical reaction or a nuclear reaction?

4. How do the control rods in a nuclear power plant control the rate of the nuclear reaction?

## Connecting the Dots

5. How is nuclear power generation similar to power generation at a geothermal power plant? How is it different?

## What Do You Think?

6. Conduct library and Internet research and write a paragraph about how and where spent nuclear fuel is stored. Write at least one paragraph describing the controversy surrounding the storage of spent fuel.

7. Dr. Steinman mentions some other applications, aside from generating electrical power, that use nuclear reactions. What are they? Conduct library and Internet research, and write a list of at least five specific technologies.

# 23

# *Down the Pipes*

## Lisa Bina

### Key Concepts
#### from Previous Chapters

Before I got my current job, I worked as a Peace Corps volunteer trying to solve a very serious problem in a small fishing village in Thailand. The hospital had been flushing untreated sewage directly into a local canal. It polluted the canal terribly and threatened to seep into the drinking water, which would have had devastating effects on the community's health. I helped to design a sewerage system to collect wastewater from the region's hospital buildings. I also helped the hospital staff construct a treatment facility that treated wastewater before it entered the open canal. While the waste treatment system was relatively simple, the steps we followed—screening out the solids then chemically treating both the solids and the remaining liquid for safe disposal—are the same complex steps we follow to treat wastewater here in the United States.

Deer Island Waste Treatment Facilities

During large storms, a Combined Sewage Overflow pipe discharges untreated sewage and storm water.

Whether you live in Thailand or the United States, waste fluids play a critical role in your community's health, as well as the health of the natural environment. My name is Lisa Bina, and today I am an engineer with the Massachusetts Water Resources Authority (MWRA). The MWRA ensures that when residents in the Greater Boston area turn on their faucets, clean water comes rushing out. The MWRA also makes sure that every time a Boston-area resident flushes a toilet, the wastewater flows for miles underground to the Deer Island Treatment Facility in Boston Harbor and finally to a large underwater tunnel to be discharged nearly ten miles out to sea. I create and run computer models that predict whether we have designed our sewers and water lines correctly.

My work in Thailand had a strong influence on my career and my commitment to my work as an environmental engineer. At the MWRA, I'm working on a similar problem. You see, the sewer system in Greater Boston was developed over hundreds of years, and parts of it are very old. Many younger cities have systems that handle rainwater and wastewater separately, but around the Boston area, this is not the case. Rainwater flows into street drains and mixes with the wastewater flowing to the Deer Island treatment facility. During major storms, the volume of water becomes too great for the pipes to carry and waste fluid backs up. In the past, to prevent the wastewater from backing up into homes, engineers built overflow points, called Combined Sewage Overflows, or CSOs, which allow the sewage and rainwater to exit the system.

Unfortunately, many of these CSOs send untreated overflow into the Boston Harbor, the Charles River, and other bodies of water. Just as it was in Thailand, it's a major problem to have untreated sewage flowing into these bodies of water—a problem that the MWRA set out to solve almost twenty years ago.

# Falling Water

Before I tell you how we're solving this problem, let me explain how our system works. Most water delivered to the taps and toilets of the Boston area is collected in the Quabbin Reservoir in Western Massachusetts. A ***reservoir*** is a natural or human-made body of water that collects and stores water for a region. Construction on the Quabbin Reservoir began in 1936. It can hold over 400 billion gallons of water when full. The Quabbin area was chosen in large part because the reservoir is about 525 feet above sea level. Because Boston is at sea level, the Quabbin is also 525 feet above Boston. This difference meant that the water would flow downhill through aqueducts—large pipes used for transporting water long distances—to Boston, driven by gravity. Pumps wouldn't be needed.

What causes water to flow downhill? If you're familiar with the effects of gravity, you know that if you hold a rock a few feet off of the ground, then let go, it will fall to the ground. But how do you explain a rock falling or water flowing downhill in terms of energy? When you raise the rock, you are doing work on the rock. The energy you are using to do work on the rock is stored in the gravitational field between the rock and the Earth (this is also called potential energy). When you let go, the energy in the gravitational field is transferred to the moving rock as it falls to the ground. Again, difference drives the energy transfer. In this case, the difference is a difference in height.

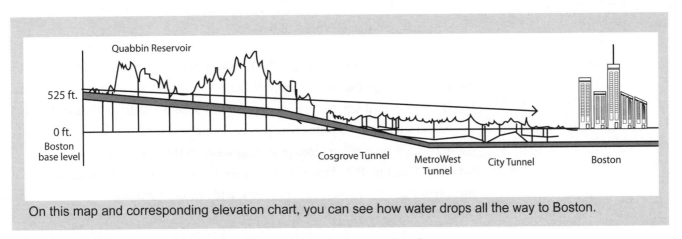

On this map and corresponding elevation chart, you can see how water drops all the way to Boston.

Difference in height causes a pressure difference and this causes fluid flow. In this case, it's a difference in height that drives change.

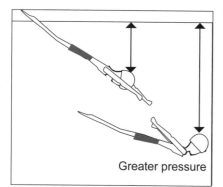
Greater pressure

The difference in the height of the water translates to a difference in pressure. The pressure, called hydrostatic pressure, is the result of the weight of the water pushing down on the water below it in the pipes.

You can better understand hydrostatic pressure by considering a diver's movement through a swimming pool. The force on the diver's head is equal to the weight of the vertical column of water through which the diver moves. As the diver swims deeper, the column of water against his head grows larger and therefore heavier. As the force of the water increases, the pressure also increases. At the very bottom of the pool, the diver's head experiences the greatest pressure.

Think of the fluid in the aqueducts of the MWRA water system like the fluid in the vertical column of water in the swimming pool. There is a difference between the pressure of the fluid at the top of the aqueduct—at elevation of 525 feet—and the pressure in an aqueduct when it reaches Boston—at sea level. Hydrostatic Pressure, $\Delta P$, can be calculated using Pascal's Equation:

$$\Delta P = \rho g\left(h_2 - h_1\right) \qquad P = \rho g \Delta h$$

where: $\rho$ is the density of the liquid and $g$ is the force due to gravity. Because p and g are constants, we can use the following equation to approximate:

$$\Delta P = \left(0.43\,\frac{\text{lb.}}{\text{in.}^2 \cdot \text{ft.}}\right)\left(h_2 - h_1\right) \quad = ?\,\text{PSI}$$

where: $h_1$ and $h_2$ are expressed in feet

The height difference between the reservoir and Boston creates enough $\Delta P$ to push water through the taps of many of the city's buildings—even the taller ones. But Boston's tallest structures require pumps to push the water to the top floors.

Pascal's equation explains why pumps are necessary. A municipality typically requires water pressure in pipes providing water to residences to measure between 50 and 60 PSI. This amount of pressure is required by most appliances that use water—toilets, taps, dishwashers, and laundry machines.

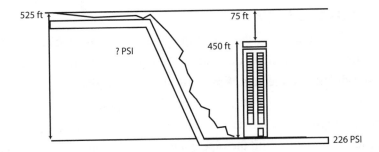

Using Pascal's Equation you can determine the pressure of the water at sea level, when $h_2$ is the elevation of the Quabbin Reservoir, and $h_1$ is the elevation at sea level:

$$\rho g = 0.43 \frac{\text{lb.}}{\text{in.}^2 \cdot \text{ft.}}$$
$$h_2 = 525 \text{ ft.}$$
$$h_1 = 0 \text{ ft.}$$
$$\Delta P = ?$$

$$\Delta P = (0.43 \frac{\text{lb.}}{\text{in.}^2 \cdot \text{ft.}})(h_2 - h_1)$$
$$\Delta P = (0.43 \frac{\text{lb}}{\text{in.}^2 \cdot \text{ft.}})(525 \text{ ft.} - 0 \text{ ft.})$$
$$\Delta P \approx 226 \text{ PSI}$$

So the pressure in the pipes at sea level is about 226 PSI. What is the pressure in the pipes on the top floor of a thirty-story building (assuming each story is fifteen feet tall)?

$$\rho g = 0.43 \frac{\text{lb.}}{\text{in.}^2 \cdot \text{ft.}}$$
$$h_2 = 525 \text{ ft.}$$
$$h_1 = 450 \text{ ft.}$$
$$\Delta P = ?$$

$$\Delta P = (0.43 \frac{\text{lb.}}{\text{in.}^2 \cdot \text{ft.}})(h_2 - h_1)$$
$$\Delta P = (0.43 \frac{\text{lb.}}{\text{in.}^2 \cdot \text{ft.}})(525 \text{ ft.} - 450 \text{ ft.})$$
$$\Delta P \approx 32.25 \text{ PSI}$$

That's not enough pressure! You can see why this building needs a pump to maintain the minimum water pressure required by household appliances.

## Going with the Flow

When a drop of rain falls into the Quabbin Reservoir, it will take as long as four years for the drop to circulate through the reservoir and find its way to a thirteen-foot-diameter aqueduct. Why do we use a large pipe to transport water long distances? That's because fluid moving through pipes encounters resistance. *Resistance* is opposition to movement. The fluid experiences the most resistance where it comes in contact with the pipe's inner wall. In smaller pipes, more fluid is exposed to the pipe's inner wall; therefore, the fluid experiences more resistance.

Water moving through a pipe is not unlike air blowing through a drinking straw. It's pretty easy to blow through a wide straw. But if you try blowing through a narrow straw, like the kind people use to stir their coffee, you'll find that you have to blow hard to get any air through the straw. The resistance reduces the flow of the air through the straw and, likewise, the flow of water through the pipes. Because we want to move large amounts of water all the way from the Quabbin to Boston, we use a large pipe in which the resistance is lower. If we used a two-foot-diameter pipe, for instance, instead of a thirteen-foot-diameter pipe, not enough water would reach the city.

Once inside an aqueduct, our water drop will travel twenty-five miles downstream (thanks to gravity) to the Wachusett Reservoir, where it will slowly move throughout the reservoir for about eight months, on average. Pumps will then draw our droplet into pipes that pass through a chlorination and fluoridation plant, which add chlorine and fluoride to the water. Chlorine cleanses the water of any bacteria; fluoride helps prevent tooth decay. The droplet will then travel downstream toward Boston. Anywhere along this path, some companion droplets may be pulled out for use by local communities. But if our droplet continues, it will flow downhill toward other smaller, covered reservoirs that serve as holding tanks for Boston and the surrounding communities.

Gravity is still driving the droplet down toward Boston. But as it approaches residential areas, the water encounters smaller pipes. Water in the large pipe moved slowly under high pressure due to the force of gravity, but the water in these smaller pipes speeds up. This fundamental principle governs the movement of liquid: as the pipe diameter decreases, the velocity of the water increases and pressure decreases.

Why is the velocity of water faster in smaller pipes? When a pipe is constricted, the volume of water flowing before the point of constriction is the same as the volume of water flowing after it. But how can the same volume of water flow through a smaller pipe? The water must move faster in a smaller pipe. As the pipe diameter decreases, the velocity of the water in the pipe increases to maintain a uniform flow rate. The relationship can be described by the following equation, in which $V_1$ is the velocity of flow in the large pipe; $V_2$ is the velocity of flow in the small pipe; $A_1$ is the cross-sectional area of the large pipe; and $A_2$ is the cross-sectional area of the small pipe:

$$V_1 \times A_1 = V_2 \times A_2$$

Imagine a pipe that has a diameter of ten inches. (Remember that the area of a circle with a radius of $r$ is equal to $\pi r^2$.) The water inside the pipe is moving at a velocity of twelve inches per second. If the pipe is constricted to a diameter of five inches, what will be the velocity of water in the constricted section of pipe?

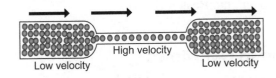

Low velocity    High velocity    Low velocity

$V_1 = 12 \frac{in}{s}$

$V_2 = ?$

$A_1 = \pi r^2 = \pi 5^2 = (25\pi)\, in.^2$

$A_2 = \pi r^2 = \pi 2.5^2 = (6.25\pi)\, in.^2$

$V_2 = V_1 \times \dfrac{A_1}{A_2}$

$V_2 = 12 \frac{in.}{s} \times \dfrac{25\pi \ in.^2}{6.25\pi \ in.^2}$

$V_2 = 12 \frac{in.}{s} \times 4$

$V_2 = 48 \frac{in.}{s}$

So you can see that as pipe size decreases, fluid velocity increases. The opposite is also true: as pipe size increases, velocity decreases. Using the same principle, water moves at higher speeds through the pipes in your home than through the pipes that get it there. Gravity brings water to large water pipes that run the length of residential streets. The higher pressure of the larger pipes pushes the water into the smaller pipes. The water is under less pressure in these smaller pipes, but it moves faster up the house pipes.

Courtesy of MWRA

Cottage Farm Treatment Facility in Cambridge, Massachusetts, treats overflow before it discharges into the Charles River.

## Love That Dirty Water

After residents use the clean water, for bathing, cooking, or toilet flushing, it becomes wastewater. When I was in Thailand, not much happened to the wastewater produced in my home. It was flushed down a small pipe and then deposited in the Earth. However, if you live in Massachusetts, the process is much more complex. On a good day, when there are no surprise storms that overwhelm the sewers, here is what happens. When a Boston resident flushes the toilet in his home, that water takes advantage of gravity to travel down to a large main sewage pipe. The large pipe, once again, uses gravity to move wastewater toward the treatment plants at Deer Island.

At Deer Island, the plants first filter out debris, such as sticks and rocks. Smaller items, such as sand, gravel, and cigarette butts, settle to the bottom of grit chambers. The organic solids are separated from the liquid wastewater. These solids, known as sludge, are mixed with bacteria in large egg-shaped digesters. The bacteria further break down the sludge. After more processing, the sludge is sent to the Sludge-to-Fertilizer Plant, where it is recycled into fertilizer products. The wastewater is sent to aeration tanks, where oxygen is added. The oxygen helps "good" bacteria to grow in the wastewater and break down contaminants. Eventually, the remaining wastewater is disinfected and discharged into a tunnel to be sent 9.5 miles out into Boston Harbor.

## Our Solution to Overflows

In a heavy storm, our systems can't handle the amount of rain entering the sewer along with the waste already in the sewer. We've worked hard to find the best way to solve this problem. Why not just build larger pipes, you might ask? Well, remember: the larger the pipe, the slower the flow. If we built pipes large enough to handle the overflow from an enormous storm, the flow would be too slow under normal weather conditions. The slow flow would lead to severe odor problems and perhaps unhealthy conditions because the wastes in the water would rot in the pipes. In addition, larger pipes are more costly to install, and if we built larger pipes to handle large rain storms, we would have to build a much larger treatment facility (which would be unused most of the time).

*Engineering the Future: Science, Technology, and the Design Process*

Copyright © 2008 Museum of Science, Boston

Another possible solution would be to create separate sewage and storm drain lines; this approach is called *sewer separation.* However, sewer separation is not always the most cost-effective solution for all areas of Boston. Some combined sewers were built up to 150 years ago. They have many connections in areas congested with pipes. To separate these areas would be very costly.

In 1994, we developed a plan to reduce the impact of the combined sewage overflows. We're using different solutions in different locations now. We found that in some areas, sewer separation works. But in other areas, we need storage tanks to hold the overflow during rainstorms. The contents of the overflow tanks later get pumped back into the system and on to the treatment facility on Deer Island. In a few other locations, we decided to build new overflow treatment facilities to disinfect the overflow before releasing it into the environment.

My main job at the MWRA is to create computer models simulating the sewer and water systems. The models have all the physical characteristics of the sewer and water systems—the length and diameter of the pipes, the elevations of the pipes, the condition of the pipes, along with other facilities that make up a system, such as pumping stations, tanks, valves, and so on. A computerized model of the system has many uses. We can use it to evaluate system improvement projects and system performance during rainstorms. We can even simulate rainstorms to evaluate system operations to determine where improvements could be made. This monitoring leads to better overall system performance.

The computer models are not perfect, but they do help us prevent some problems from occurring again. Prevention has led to major improvements to the environmental well-being of my community. Since the 1980s, the volume of wastewater overflows has been reduced by 70 percent, and 60 percent of the wastewater that does overflow is now treated. As we optimize our system even more, the environmental quality and health of the harbor and local rivers will get better and better. It gives me great satisfaction to be a part of that effort. After all, whether people live in Thailand or the United States, their health depends on clean water and a healthy environment. I became an environmental engineer so I could help to provide both.

## What's the Story?

1. In what ways was Lisa's work in Thailand and the United States similar?

2. What problem does Lisa describe in Boston's sewage system?

3. How is a reservoir different from a lake?

## Designing with Math and Science

4. Why is the location of a reservoir significant?

5. What is the maximum height water will flow up into a skyscraper in Boston without the need to use pumps?

6. What happens to the velocity of water as the diameter of the pipe in which it flows is decreased?

7. Why can't engineers handle excess wastewater problems by designing a system with larger pipes?

## What Do You Think?

8. Lisa is an environmental engineer. Use the library or the Internet to do some research on the field of environmental engineering. What other kinds of jobs do environmental engineers hold?

9. Do reservoirs ever get too full? What happens in a drought? Find out how much water your local drinking water reservoir can hold, and find out when backup reservoirs would be activated in a drought situation.

# Power to Communicate

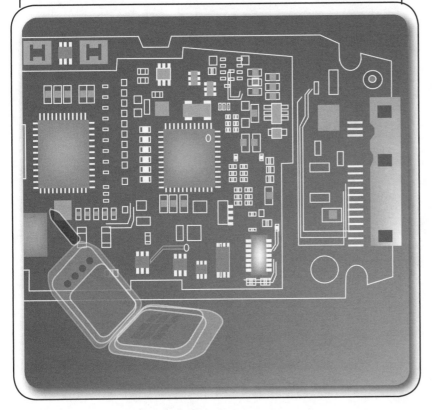

# 24

## *A Highway for Ideas*

## David Clark

*Courtesy of David Clark*

### 🔧 Key Concepts
**from Previous Chapters**

1️⃣ Process

1️⃣ Researching the Problem

1️⃣ Building the Prototype

1️⃣ Testing the Prototype

Scientists attempt to understand the world as it is. Engineers, on the other hand, take the principles from science and ask, "What is possible? Am I limited by what I know or can I reach further? Can I look at today's scientific understandings with new eyes and create something that has never existed before?" When an engineer invents something that profoundly changes the world, such as the telephone or the computer, you could say that the engineer has turned science into a constructive art, an art of the imagination. Many believe that in the virtual space of the Internet, the only real limit is our imagination. That's exactly what the creators of the Internet envisioned.

My name is David Clark, and I am a computer scientist. I teach network engineering and design at the Massachusetts Institute of Technology (MIT). Some people refer to me as one of the "fathers" of the Internet because I was on the team that designed it. I like to refer to myself as the Internet's "first cousin."

That's because so many people had a hand in developing a way for people in different locations to exchange information by linking their computers together.

Those of us on that design team never imagined that the Internet would become the incredible resource it is today. It makes information about any topic available to any user 24 hours a day, and allows people from different cultures, languages, nations, and religions to gather on common ground. Who could have foreseen that the Internet would become so widespread that people would have trouble thinking of what the world may have been like before? Many young people today have a hard time imagining life without downloadable music, Instant Messenger, e-mail, or the World Wide Web.

The roots of the Internet can be traced all the way back to World War II and its aftermath, when the United States started investing more in science and engineering to ensure a better future for our country and the world. These were complex times for the United States. In the 1940s and 1950s, society witnessed how scientists and engineers could alter the course of history. A group of researchers and engineers involved in the Manhattan Project created the first nuclear bomb by 1945. The bombs dropped on two cities in Japan, ending World War II, led to the loss of hundreds of thousands of lives. In the early 1950s, President Eisenhower oversaw the creation of the national interstate highway system. Very quickly, Americans achieved a mobility enjoyed by no other nation, but we also have suffered the unintended consequences of the automobile's widespread use.

Perhaps most importantly, in 1957 the former Soviet Union launched Sputnik, the first man-made satellite to orbit the Earth. At the time, the United States was involved in the "cold war" with the Soviet Union, a nation that has since dissolved into Russia and several countries in Eastern Europe and Central Asia. The U.S. competed with the Soviet Union for military, economic, and technological superiority. At the time, Sputnik symbolized a major victory for the Soviets by beating the U.S. into space. In response, the U.S. Defense Department established the Defense Advanced Research Projects Agency (DARPA) to keep the U.S. ahead in using technology. The U.S. launched its own satellite within four months.

Sputnik was the first artificial satellite put into orbit.

DARPA quickly turned its attention to what was then an emerging technology: computers. In 1960 there were no desktop computers, only large mainframe computers that filled whole rooms. Personal computers—or PCs— would not arrive on the scene for another 20 years. Most people who used computers were researchers at universities or those working in the government. Only the biggest of companies could afford their own computer. While these computers could process large amounts of data and store files, they weren't used for much else.

In the 1960s, engineers and computer scientists developed many of the important computer technologies we now take for granted. This includes software for sharing computers among many users, graphical displays (without which we would have no computer games today), and the computer disk (without which we would not be able to store all our music, mail, and files on our computers).

Around that time, DARPA started focusing on a new problem: networking the computers of research groups at universities and government labs. They thought that such a network might allow researchers to work together to advance the state of science and technology in America. So DARPA assembled a group of computer scientists to figure out just how to do that. First they built something called ARPAnet, the Advanced Research Project Agency Network. In the 1970s, they started on the Internet. That is when I joined the project.

## Designing the Net

What would the Internet be like if you had designed it? Would it be any different than it is now? It's a question few people stop to ask themselves. The Internet, after all, seems like a huge, chaotic marketplace for ideas that is not controlled by anyone. It's hard to imagine that someone might have designed it to be that way. But we did—quite intentionally.

You see, as we designed the Internet, we drew inspiration from another new technology that was similar to what we wanted to create: the interstate highway system.

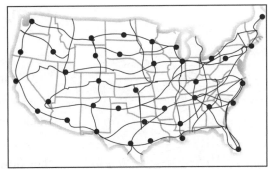

A map of the interstate highway system

Why a highway system? Highways give users a lot of freedom. The engineers who designed the highway placed few limits on how vehicles were to be designed. They only made three main rules: a vehicle must have some type of power source to propel it; it must roll along the highway without destroying the surface of the road; and it must fit onto a highway lane.

It was up to vehicle designers to figure out the best vehicle design given those constraints. Yes, a car might use a combustion engine, but the highway itself does not require that. The engine could run on solar power, electricity, or natural gas—or even some power source not yet created. Sure, other forces such as the availability of fuel, national and state laws, or economics might affect an automobile design. But the highway itself imposed only a few restrictions. It simply provided a path for moving the machines.

In the early seventies, when we were coming up with the Internet's design, we knew that new communications technologies would emerge in the next several decades. But we had no idea what they would be. Satellites had just been launched, television was becoming mainstream, and the telephone system in the country was well established. Telephone systems were so well established that we decided to use telephone wires to connect the computers in our system. Fiber-optic cables, which allow for rapid transit of information across distances, did not yet exist, nor did CDs or DVDs. Those technologies all came later. We wanted to create a system that would be flexible enough to accommodate new technologies, like the highway system. Our system would not limit what traveled along its paths; it would only provide a way for the information to get from point A to point B.

## Computer Science 101

Before I describe the rules we created for the Internet, you need to understand a few basic concepts about how computers function.

Computers are electronic devices that process electrical signals. The "brains" of a computer, called the ***motherboard,*** is a very complex, interconnected set of electronic devices, processor, memory, and control chips. The chips contain transistors, which are basically on-off switches that control electrical signals as they flow through the circuits. These transistors are made out of semiconductors. ***Semiconductors*** conduct currents, but not as well as a true conductor, such as copper. This makes semiconductors excellent materials for controlling the flow of electricity through a circuit.

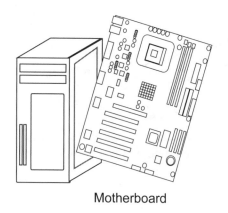

Motherboard

Computers recognize two states: the presence of an electrical signal or the absence of the electrical signal. In other words, they recognize when the signal is on or off. People have given the "on" and "off" signals numerical values so that they are easier for us to work with. The "on" signal is referred to as one, while the "off" signal is referred to as zero. You've probably heard of bits and bytes. A bit is a 1 or a 0. A byte is a string of eight bits.

So how does a computer process very complex information when it only recognizes two digits? Well, if you think about it, we only use ten digits, 0 through 9, which is called a base 10, or *decimal,* system. A computer describes every number, no matter how large, with 1s and 0s. So the computer uses a base 2, or binary, system, which we call binary code.

Every letter of the alphabet has been assigned a corresponding number in binary code. For instance, when a person taps the letter "D" on a computer keyboard, it will turn transistors on and off in the following pattern: 01000100. This code is called ASCII (American Standard Code for Information Interchange) and is pronounced "ask-kee."

The strings of bits and bytes, made up of the ones and zeros that a computer reads, can be represented as *digital signals.* Digital signals are not continuous, but are made up of a discrete, limited set of elements. Many other communications signals are not digital. Electrical signals used in older telephone system were all *analog signals.* Analog signals are continuous and vary within some range, rather than using an on and off pattern. The graph of an analog signal is a continuous wave, with peaks and valleys.

|   | Binary |
|---|---|
| 0 | 0 |
| 1 | 1 |
| 2 | 10 |
| 3 | 11 |
| 4 | 100 |
| 5 | 101 |
| 6 | 110 |
| 7 | 111 |
| 8 | 1000 |
| 9 | 1001 |
| 10 | 1010 |

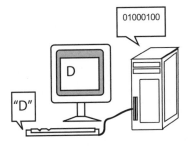

**ASCII**

| Letter | Binary |
|---|---|
| A | 01000001 |
| B | 01000010 |
| C | 01000011 |
| D | 01000100 |
| E | 01000101 |
| F | 01000110 |
| G | 01000111 |

An *analog signal* ranges over a continuous set of values.

A *digital signal* has a discrete limited set of numerical values, such as bits and bytes.

## The "Rules" of the Internet

Now that you know something about the digital nature of computers, I can explain the limits Internet users face. Again, those of us on the original design team didn't want to limit users, but we did have to establish some ground rules.

### 1. Information Must Be Digital

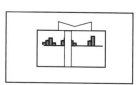

The first Internet connected distant computers using analog signals over a telephone line. We wanted to make sure that the Internet could carry all sorts of data. Some of the data was created inside the computers, the programs, and data files. This data needs to be carried in digital form, which is how it was created. In addition, there are other analog signals besides voice, including music, television, and scanned images. The Internet needed to carry all these as well. So we decided that the Internet would transport digital bits, knowing that any analog signal could be converted to a digital signal (a sequence of zeros and ones).

We settled on the idea of **data packets,** which are discrete packages of information. The data packets could contain any type of data as long as it was encoded by the computer into digital form. Then a modem, a communication device, would convert the digital signal from the computer into an analog signal before sending it over the telephone network. You can hear these signals today when a modem first connects. The tones, whistles, and buzzes are in the same frequencies that we use in speech, so they are carried by the telephone system quite naturally.

We also decided that it would be the user's responsibility to create data that could be encoded as a digital signal. The Internet's job would be to move these data packets along as efficiently as possible without any concern for what information the packets contained.

### 2. Every Computer on the Network Must Have an Address

We needed to ensure that the system could deliver data to the correct recipient. We decided that every computer would have an address, just like how every home or business has a postal address. Today, every computer on the Internet has an IP, or Internet Protocol, address. Internet addresses are thirty-two bits long, expressed as a binary number, but we often write them down in a more convenient form.

You may have seen an Internet address. It looks like "71.232.4.16," four sets of numbers separated by dots. Each data packet is labeled with the address of the recipient. Routers located along the Internet pathway make sure that the data packets follow the shortest path possible to the addressee.

## 3. Packets Can Only Be So Large

As you may know, a data file can be very large. It may be a huge text file or contain graphic images or even short movies. We knew that hundreds and maybe thousands of computers would be sending files of all sizes across the Internet. (Little did we know that millions of users would one day communicate through the Internet!) If each computer had to wait for another computer on the network to send its data, the computers sending the largest messages would clog the network, making it difficult for shorter messages to get through in a reasonable period of time.

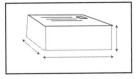

Waiting for a big message to get through would be like standing in line at the grocery store behind someone buying several carts full of groceries. The lines move fastest when customers limit the number of items in a shopping cart to ten or fifteen items. So imagine if store management did not allow anyone to pass through the checkout with more than fifteen items. A person with sixty items would have to pay for fifteen items, go to the back of the line, submit another fifteen items through the checkout, then return to the back of the line two more times to complete the sale. While this person had to go through the line four times, many others would be able to finish shopping quickly.

So our design team decided to limit the size of each packet. The actual limit has changed over time, but today each data packet sent over the Internet is normally no more than 1,500 bytes. If someone needs to send 3,000 bytes of information, the message is split into two packets. If the message is 30,000 bytes large, it is split into twenty packets.

## 4. Packets Must Be Sequenced

Now, in addition to carrying the address of the receiving computer, each data packet also has to have a sequence number so that the receiving computer can reassemble the message in the correct order. If there were no sequence numbers, it would be like sending several postcards to a friend without numbering the postcards. Your friend would not understand the message until all the postcards arrived, and then only if she could figure out the right sequence.

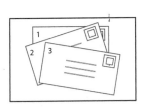

Routers along the system have only one set of tasks: read the address, locate the receiving machine, and send the packet over the fastest route available. It does not matter to the routers what is contained in the message. It could be a video transmission from CNN or someone in the Alaskan countryside sending an e-mail to a friend in New Jersey. The routers are intentionally designed to ignore the content being delivered.

Those are the four key constraints that our design imposed: Senders are responsible for encoding a message as bits and bytes on the sending side, and receivers must decode it for their own purposes on the receiving side; digital information must be broken up into small packets; each packet has to have a clear address and each has to have a sequence number. That's it. As long as a user has a connection to the Internet and followed these rules, he can send anything he wants over the Internet.

## Designing for Innovation

You will notice that these principles do not tell you anything about how to build the actual network technology. They do not define how fast the links go; whether the network uses wires, fiber optics, or radio; or whether the network hooks up 10 computers or 10,000. Any kind of communication technology that can carry bits may be put to use as part of the Internet.

The first network that carried Internet packets was the original ARPAnet. Then a wireless network and a satellite network were added. When the PC was invented, and local area networks (or LANs) were deployed, those got hooked in as well. Then the interconnected set of networks called the Internet started to grow across the country and across the globe.

The next step in the growth of the Internet occurred in the eighties, when the National Science Foundation (NSF), a government organization that funds research, developed a program to start linking all of the different networks together with one "backbone." This started out being built out of phone lines, and ended up as a massive high-speed fiber-optic cable "super highway."

The NSF encouraged all kinds of users—not just researchers—to join these networks. In time, private companies such as America Online got into the game, offering users access to the Internet for a fee. Since the early days of ARPAnet, the Internet has grown into a giant web of users some 800 million strong!

Internet users are not restricted by the limits of older technologies and older versions. New technologies like Ethernet, wireless, and fiber optics have been incorporated. New applications such as the Web, voiceover IP (voIP), and multiplayer games have been devised and deployed. The same is true for the development of streaming video and Internet telephone.

That's what we had in mind. We were never sure what would happen, but we wanted to help it along, whatever "it" might become. So we designed the Internet to promote innovation. When Tim Berner-Lees, a computer programmer, figured out how to use the Internet to host Web pages, and created the World Wide Web, he didn't come ask for our permission. We didn't have to change anything about the Internet. He just followed the conventions for data packets and addressing and then went about developing a method for presenting information on interactive "pages." His pioneering work totally transformed the way we find information.

No one has to ask to use the Internet. If you want to teach classes to students 200 miles away, or consult with a physician in another country, you just do it. So long as the messages you send are broken into digital packets, properly addressed, and sequenced, you can do just about anything on the Internet.

The Age of the Internet is far from over. In some respects, that age will never end. It will simply evolve into a new form as new innovations replace the old. As computers evolve, from PCs to laptops to PDAs and even smaller, smarter devices, the Internet will evolve to hook them all together. From the initial modest goal of transferring files from one computer to another, a new chapter in the history of our society has begun. Now an entire world of users can collaborate to build the system called the Internet, giving it a life of its own. We are all engineers when it comes to building this virtual space.

## What's the Story?

1. What major historical events led to the formation of the Internet?

2. What problems were the developers of the Internet trying to solve?

3. What are the design constraints placed on Internet users?

4. Why must data packets be small and sequenced?

## Designing with Math and Science

5. What's the difference between an analog signal and a digital signal? Give examples of each.

## What Do You Think?

6. In your opinion, what are some of the key ways the Internet has affected our society?

7. Do you believe its a good thing that anyone can put anything (or find anything) online? What are some of the unintended consequences of that freedom?

# 25

## Teaching a Machine to Listen

### Sol Lerner

Photo taken by John Ost

---

### Key Concepts
**from Previous Chapters**

**7** Systems

**24** Digital and Analog Signals

**24** Data Transfer

---

New technologies have altered the way humans communicate. These include cell phones, faxes, web cameras, instant message programs, and more. Some might argue that these technologies have changed our society for the worse, that people now prefer the company of a computer to real human contact. Personally, I think the technologies of the Information Age have brought all of us closer together. New communications systems help us to exchange ideas and information quickly with each other, regardless of our physical limitations, differences in language and culture, or our geographic location.

Besides, I find it fascinating how machines do it. My name is Sol Lerner, and I work at a company called Scansoft, where I develop speech recognition systems—programs that allow computers to recognize and interpret the words people say.

Computers respond to spoken language by running preprogrammed tasks. Many speech recognition systems display on the screen what a person says into a microphone. Other systems have a conversation with the person, much like a human would, in order to provide a service, such as checking flight information. Scansoft is an industry leader in speech recognition. In fact, we created Dragon Naturally Speaking, which is the number-one-selling speech recognition software available today.

My job is to improve voice recognition systems by attempting to understand the rules humans use to communicate with sounds. I work in the field of artificial intelligence, which makes me part of a long history of scientists and engineers interested in writing programs that allow computers to "think" more like humans. Of course, a computer can't really think. Instead, it follows incredibly intricate sets of rules that allow it to respond to different stimuli in complex ways—much like a human would. But, because spoken language is so complex, a computer must be smart in order to decipher spoken words accurately.

Why are we so interested in doing this? Well, people with injuries to their hands, with chronic arthritis, or who are paralyzed or have impaired vision may have difficulty using a keyboard. Without voice recognition systems like the ones I've worked on, these people would be unable to use a computer to work, play, or communicate.

Scansoft has also developed speech recognition systems for telephone service requests. Now, when calling a business, instead of a person answering the phone, you'll often hear a computerized voice asking, "How can I help you?" When you speak, the computer responds to the key words in your request and routes the call to the correct extension.

Given all that computers can do these days, it may seem that designing such a system would be easy. In fact, it's a real dilemma. Everyone's voice is different. Many people speak with different accents, and even the way we speak can make it difficult for a computer to make sense of what we say. But in the past couple of years we've greatly improved our system's ability to recognize words and sentences. Now, some of our software, which allows a computer to display words as someone speaks, is accurate more than 95 percent of the time, after the software has been programmed to understand the user's voice.

So how do you design and build a communications system that allows humans to use their voice to interact with a machine? First, let's look at a simple communication system: the telephone. When using a telephone, you transmit your message by speaking into a microphone, sometimes called a mouthpiece. Sound waves from your voice strike a diaphragm, making it vibrate. In a simple microphone, carbon granules are compressed between two disks; the diaphragm, which consists of a thin disk; and a backing plate. The vibrating diaphragm compresses and decompresses the carbon granules inside this chamber, changing their resistance. When connected to a low-voltage electric circuit, the changing resistance of the granules also varies the current flowing through the circuit. The microphone translates the sound wave information from your voice into electrical current patterns called a signal. The electrical signal, which encodes the sound waves of your voice, carries the information through wires to a second telephone.

The speaker, or receiver, of the second telephone receives the electrical signal, which the speaker translates or decodes into sound waves that we recognize as speech. The speaker also has a diaphragm, as well as two magnets. One is a permanent magnet that constantly holds the diaphragm near it. The other is an electromagnet, usually made of iron, wrapped with a coil of wire. When an electric current passes through the coil of wire, the iron core becomes magnetized, pulling the diaphragm away from the first magnet toward the iron core. The pull of the magnet duplicates the changes in the electric current pattern, causing the diaphragm to vibrate, which moves the air forward and back and decodes your original message.

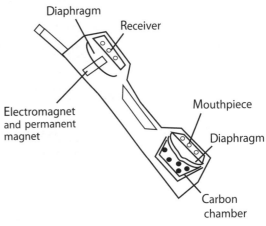

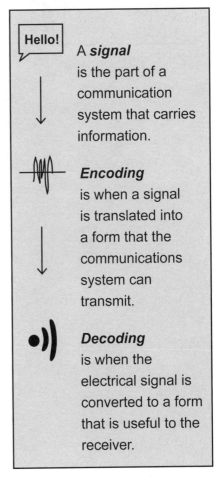

A *signal* is the part of a communication system that carries information.

*Encoding* is when a signal is translated into a form that the communications system can transmit.

*Decoding* is when the electrical signal is converted to a form that is useful to the receiver.

## Recognizing Speech

Systems such as the telephone are great at encoding, decoding, and transmitting signals. So getting a computer to "hear" human speech is relatively easy. The electrical signal is transmitted to a computer in the same way as the telephone. The computer converts the *analog* signal into binary code, a *digital* signal of ones and zeros.

But only recently have we started trying to design systems to do what the human brain does so remarkably well—understand the spoken word. Because a computer system does not have a human brain to interpret what the signals mean, scientists like myself must give the system enough information to do so on its own.

That's what I do every day at Scansoft, and it's an incredibly complex task. The computer needs to be programmed with the intricate set of rules that govern speech. Why not just catalog every word spoken in every dialect of English? If we did that, we would have a database of several hundred thousand words, and because language is constantly changing, the database would never be complete. Fortunately, every language has a much smaller group of distinct sounds. By identifying the frequencies that represent each sound, the computer can scan any cluster of signals that it receives and identify it as a particular word, letter, or sound.

Unfortunately, spoken language is not that straightforward. You may use the same sounds to express any number of ideas. For example, "I know you ate the cake" has the same sounds as "Eye no ewe 8 the cake." Human listeners can tell the difference between the two phrases because our brains use our own set of rules; we interpret the sounds how and when they are used. We know that the word "cake" is more likely to show up next to the word "ate" than the number "8." We also know from our experience that "Eye no ewe 8 the cake" does not make sense.

I spend my time analyzing language and trying to understand and make use of all of the rules that we use when we speak or hear. For example, I might create a rule that the word "bat" is often used with the verb "hit" and the noun "ball" and is often linked with "sports."

As soon as the computer recognizes the signal pattern for "B – A – T" and it recognizes the signals and sound patterns for "THE," it might be able to "understand" the sentence:

THE/ B A T / _ _ T / T H E / B A _ _/.

By following the rules we created for associating "hit" and "ball" and linked with sports, it can then predict that the sentence is:

THE/ B A T / H I T / T H E / B A L L/.

Whenever I travel to other parts of the country, I meet with clients who speak English differently than I do. Have you ever noticed how different a word sounds when it is spoken by someone from another part of the country? Southerners may draw out their vowels while people on the west coast clip their consonants, speaking in a punctuated rhythm. If you come from Pennsylvania, you are likely to say "yes" or "no" to a question. But a person in central Florida might answer by saying "Yes, Sir" or "No, Ma'am"—even to a machine. A computer programmed to respond to just "yes" would not be able to process "Yes, Sir." People also may have any combination of different speech patterns, depending on what city, state, or country they have lived in. So there are real challenges to developing a program that allows software to recognize any person's voice.

When it comes to developing voice recognition systems that work across languages and cultures, the challenges are endless. It might be a long time before we can develop a system that truly recognizes speech as well as humans can. It'll be much longer before we can make a computer that "thinks" or even "feels." We have only just started on the right path to solve those problems. Right now, there is no doubt that we can communicate through and with machines more easily than ever. Whether or not you believe that's a good thing, it's the reality of our time.

## What's the Story?

1. What reasons does Sol offer for wanting to develop speech recognition systems?

2. Why is it challenging to design a computer system that can recognize and interpret human speech?

## Designing with Math and Science

3. What's the difference between a signal and a message?

4. What parts of the telephone communications system are the encoder and the decoder? What is being encoded? Why is encoding necessary?

## Connecting the Dots

5. How is electricity used in the two communications systems described in this chapter?

## What Do You Think?

6. What are some other ways that humans communicate with or through machines?

7. Sol says that technologies have brought people closer together, but some people disagree. Do you agree? Explain why or why not.

# 26

# Shedding Light on Communications

Nanette Halliburton

Courtesy of Nanette Halliburton

**Key Concepts**
**from Previous Chapters**

24 Digital and Analog Signals

24 Binary Code

25 Encoder, Decoder

If you've ever sent an e-mail, you've experienced the "magic" that happens when you click "send." Your message zips away and may travel hundreds or even thousands of miles in a few minutes to show up in your friend's inbox. Of course, it's hardly magical. You already know that information can travel as sound, as radio waves, and through wires as an electrical signal. Today, a relatively new technology can use light to transmit information over distances. Yes, visible light—the colors of the rainbow! In fact, most e-mails travel encoded as a light signal for some portion of their journey.

Before I explain why light is such a popular way to move information around, let me tell you a bit about myself. My name is Nanette Halliburton, and, as a test engineer with Cisco Systems, Inc., I evaluate the equipment that converts encoded analog and digital signals into light signals.

I've always had a passion for technical subjects. When I was young, I used to follow my uncle around while he worked. He liked to fix cars and tinker with things. Because I had small hands, he was always asking me to reach into places where his hands didn't fit. I was curious and inquisitive, always asking questions about how things worked. I was a willing student as my uncle explained the inner workings of a carburetor or an air conditioner. Each new machine that he worked on was like a puzzle, and I asked questions until I understood how the pieces fit together. I found it fascinating how the laws of physics applied to the tools and machines that we use every day. I still do.

Because of my interest in technology, I decided to go to a specialized high school in New York City, the Murray Bergtraum High School for Business Careers, where I studied computer science. After graduation, I applied to a very competitive engineering program at Syracuse University in New York, but I was only accepted into their Liberal Arts program. I was disappointed, but I decided not to let that stop me. At Syracuse, I took every computer and electronics course that the engineering majors took. Hard work paid off. I eventually was accepted into the engineering program and finished my degree in electrical engineering.

## The Long Haul

At Cisco, my department develops and manufactures long-haul equipment—devices that transmit data in the form of light over long distances. Using fiber-optic cables, our equipment transmits light signals for thousands of miles, even across the ocean floor. But the signal must be regenerated every so often. After 50 or 60 miles, the light signal is amplified and retransmitted using an optical regenerator.

Typically, these long-haul cable lines run between major cities—from New York to Washington, D.C., for instance. Cisco installs these systems for telephone companies all over the country. Every day fiber-optic cable is replacing good ol' copper telephone lines for sending data over long distances.

Why use fiber-optic cable instead of copper wire? Each phone line consists of a bundle of wires, and each wire carries different signals. Telephones transmit encoded signals using an electrical current and, as you know, any time you run current through a wire, it creates a magnetic field around the wire.

The magnetic fields created by these wire bundles may interfere with the signals traveling in the wires. This interference, called *noise*, can garble words and cause hissing and static. Due to this noise, the electrical signal must be regenerated every mile or so along the wire. Fiber optics eliminate this noise, improving the clarity of the signal.

*Noise* is anything that interferes with the clarity of a message.

## Bouncing off the Walls

So how do we get light to travel through a cable? Thanks to the basic physics of how light travels, it's not nearly as complicated as it sounds. As a small part of the electromagnetic spectrum, visible light moves at a very high speed, around 300,000 kilometers, or 186,000 miles, per second in a vacuum. Light slows down in denser mediums such as our atmosphere and travels a little slower in water.

Light radiates in all directions until it strikes an object, where it can be absorbed, reflected, or refracted. An object that *absorbs* light heats up. A blacktop road gets very hot because much of the light energy from the sun is transferred to the road. When light bounces off objects, we see the color that the object *reflects.* Different materials reflect different frequencies of the visible light spectrum. A red apple reflects light in the red frequency, while a green apple reflects light in the green frequency. Each object absorbs the other light frequencies that are not seen. The black road appears black because it absorbs all of the visible light that hits it, reflecting no color at all. On the contrary, a page of white paper reflects all frequencies of visible light and therefore appears white.

During *absorption* the energy of a light wave is transferred to and heats up an object.

During *reflection* the energy of a light wave bounces off an object.

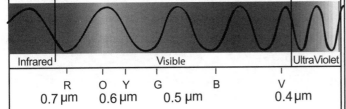

Visible Light Region of Electromagnetic Spectrum

| Infrared | Visible | UltraViolet |
|---|---|---|
| | R     O   Y     G       B       V | |
| | 0.7 µm   0.6 µm   0.5 µm         0.4 µm | |

During **refraction,** light passes from one medium into another. Imagine shining a flashlight into a tub of water in a dark room. The light beam travels through the air into the water. The refracted light bends as it moves from the air into the denser water, because the speed of light decreases slightly. The amount that the light bends is called the angle of refraction.

Now imagine a light being directed through water to the air. Water is denser than air. As the angle of the light beam gets closer to being parallel to the surface of the air, you'll find that, at a certain angle, the light does not enter the air but reflects back. When the angle of the light is large enough to bend all the light back into the water, it is called ***total internal reflection.*** The minimum angle for total internal reflection is called the critical angle. The critical angle is 48.6 degrees for light passing from water to air.

An optical fiber takes advantage of this property. A cable is a bundle of individual fibers, or long, thin strands of glass. A single fiber is no thicker than a human hair, which measures, on average, about 80 microns, or 0.000080 meters. The solid glass fiber is called the core, which is coated with a glass material called cladding.

When a light beam is flashed at one end of the fiber, the light enters the fiber and angles toward all the sides of the tubing. When the light hits the cladding, it is reflected. Because the speed of light in the fiber is significantly different from the speed of light in the cladding, total internal reflection occurs and the light is directed right back into the core. The cladding acts like a mirror, reflecting the light back toward the center of the core, keeping the beam focused and strong.

If the glass in the fiber were 100 percent pure, the light signal would never degrade or weaken as it travels down the cable at the speed of light. But no matter how carefully we manufacture the fiber, we can't make it perfectly pure. Other elements mix in with the glass and absorb some of the light. The cladding may contain impurities as well, which allows some light to leak out, weakening the signal. To combat this, optical regenerators strengthen the signal every fifty or sixty miles.

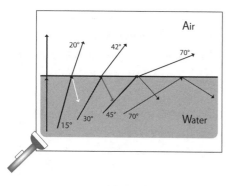

Refraction occurs because the speed of light in one material is different than the speed of light in the second. You can see that as the light-beam angle becomes greater, more light is reflected instead of refracted. Past a certain critical angle, all of the light is reflected. To have a critical angle, light must pass from a denser medium to less dense medium. There is a critical angle for water to air but not for air to water.

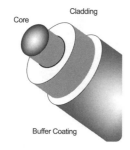

An added advantage of using light is that each fiber can carry multiple signals by using different light frequencies. Optical fibers are also smaller than wires, so even though hundreds of fibers make up each optical cable, noise is eliminated. This means that the phone calls you make are clearer, data moves faster, and video streams—television signals and video you watch on a computer—are crisper and look more realistic.

## From Analog to Digital

While I've explained how light travels through optical fiber, you may be asking, how do we encode messages as light signals? To send a light signal, a transmitter translates an analog electric signal into a matching digital pattern that turns a laser on and off. The flashes of light last for only a small fraction of a second, so many thousands of encoded bytes can be sent very quickly. At the end of the cable, a light-sensitive cell receives the light signal and translates it back into an electrical signal.

Now that you have a sense of how fiber optics carry light information, you can start to understand how an e-mail can travel hundreds and thousands of miles in a matter of minutes. The signal containing the e-mail message may change forms many times along the way. Say you are visiting Washington, D.C., and you send an e-mail to a friend in Raleigh, North Carolina, telling her about your trip to the Smithsonian. In order for the e-mail to travel from your computer to your friend's computer, it takes a very long journey in a very short time. Let's trace the journey.

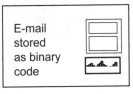

Analog to digital conversion

### Step 1: Typing the E-Mail

When you type and save your message, the computer stores it as a binary code.

### Step 2: Sending the Message

When you click "send," the computer sends out an encoded digital signal containing your e-mail and the address of the recipient to the modem. If you connect to the Internet using a telephone, your modem converts the digital signal into an analog signal that can travel as electrical current along telephone wires.

E-mail stored as binary code

Modem-digital to analog

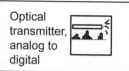

Travel via telephone wire

Optical transmitter, analog to digital

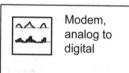

ISP creates data packets

Light signals travel through cable

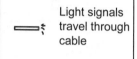

Digital to analog, travel via phone line

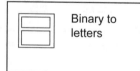

Modem, analog to digital

Binary to letters

### Step 3: Going Optical

The message, now an encoded analog signal, moves through the telephone wires to the local telephone company in Washington, D.C. There the signal meets an optical transmitter, perhaps one that Cisco designed and manufactured. The optical transmitter first converts the signal to a binary encoded digital signal. It then turns a laser light on and off to match the sequence of the signal. The light beam, created by a laser, shoots down the fiber-optic cable toward your Internet service provider (ISP) at close to 186,000 miles per second.

### Step 4: Getting on the Information Super Highway

Your ISP now breaks the data into discrete packets small enough to be sent over the Internet. Each data packet is labeled with the Internet address of your friend's computer. Devices called routers act as network connectors. They determine which way to send data so that it follows the fastest path to your friend's ISP in North Carolina. Once again, these packets are sent as light signals through the fiber-optic cable. Every 50 or 60 miles, the packets are received, amplified, and retransmitted. This regeneration continues until the signal is received at your friend's ISP in Raleigh, which converts and stores the message in binary code.

### Step 5: Back to the Computer

When your friend in Raleigh connects to her ISP to receive her e-mails, your e-mail is translated again into an analog signal and sent over the local phone line to her home. The modem receives the signal, converts it to a digital signal, and transmits it to the computer. The computer decodes the signal one last time, and the e-mail becomes text that your friend can read. When you think about it, there is one more conversion: Her eyes convert the graphics, the letters, numbers, and even pictures into electrical signals that her brain can understand!

# Phew! Talk about a long journey!

Amazingly enough, the system can move e-mail to anywhere in the world in a matter of minutes. If you're connected to the Internet using a cable connection to your ISP, it happens even faster. That's because your message bypasses the telephone system and connects directly to your ISP and the Internet.

So, what makes my job interesting and important? At Cisco, I test optical transport systems. I write computer programs that trick devices into encoding, regenerating, and delivering signals as if actual data had been received. That way I can make sure that each device will have the appropriate response before we hook it up to the network. Imagine if these devices often failed on the job. That would create a terrible information traffic jam!

My role in maintaining the information superhighway may seem pretty specialized. Afterall, I only work on a small part of the information super highway. But testing is just as important as designing and building. If I don't do my small part well, the communications infrastructure on which so many individuals, businesses, governments, and research institutions depend could come to a screeching halt. That's one thing I love about working with technology. Every system is like a puzzle, and all of its pieces must fit—and work—together properly.

## The E-Mail Journey

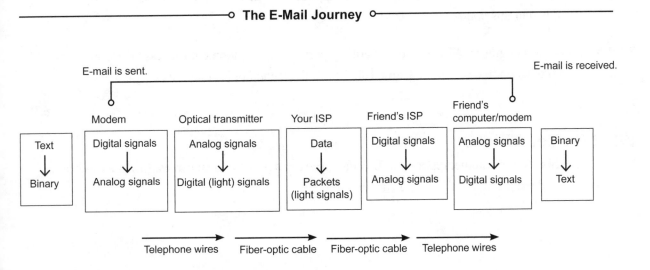

## What's the Story?

1. What does noise refer to in this chapter?

2. Why are fiber-optic cables better than telephone wires for transmitting information over long distances?

## Designing with Math and Science

3. Explain how light travels through a fiber-optic cable, using the terms "reflection" and "total internal reflection."

4. Why does the light signal have to be regenerated?

5. How can ones and zeros be encoded in a light signal?

## Connecting the Dots

6. Nanette talks about how every technological system is like a puzzle, that all of its pieces must fit—and work—together properly. Describe how this applies to at least two other technological systems you've studied in this course.

7. Nanette is a test engineer. Why is testing a critical part of the development process? Describe how at least two other engineers you've learned about test the technologies they've designed.

## What Do You Think?

8. Do some library and Internet research to find the disadvantages of optical cables. Consider the cable materials and the installation processes in your response.

# 27

## *Riding the Waves*

### Alex Hills

**Key Concepts**
**from Previous Chapters**

**18** Radiation

**25** Signals

My whole life, I've been driven by a desire to explore unknown lands and cultures. When I was a teenager growing up near New York City, I started using shortwave radio to "travel" to exotic destinations—without ever leaving my home. My friends and I sat in my bedroom and sent out Morse code messages to other "ham" radio operators around the world. Little did I know then that my passion for radio would contribute to a revolution in the way people communicate.

My name is Alex Hills, and I'm a professor of engineering and public policy at Carnegie Mellon University in Pittsburgh, Pennsylvania. I've spent a lot of time in Alaska, though, where I've worked on developing satellite communications systems. I'm also one of the originators of wireless fidelity, or "Wi-Fi"— the technology that allows you to access the Internet from your laptop without wires.

Here I am in the 1970s.

I studied electrical engineering and communications at Rensselaer Polytechnic Institute in New York. Soon after graduation, I got a job working as a design engineer for IBM on a "super computer" called the System 360 Model 95. At the time, it was the largest and fastest computer in the world, and it occupied almost an entire room. But working in an office didn't satisfy my urge to travel or my quest for adventure.

After receiving a graduate degree in electrical engineering from Arizona State University, I was offered a chance to build and manage one of the first public radio stations in Alaska. How could I possibly turn down an opportunity that included adventure, radio, and engineering? So, at the age of 28, I headed to Alaska. Two years later, I became the field leader of an RCA Alaska Communications Project, building a telephone network for people living in the Alaskan bush. My job was to provide a way for people in these remote regions of Alaska to communicate with the rest of the state.

In 1970, Alaska did not have a telecommunications network, except in cities like Anchorage, Fairbanks, and Juneau. In the cities, people lived close together, so it was economically practical to install telephone cables and build a telephone system similar to those in the rest of the country.

But in the small outlying villages in the bush, the residents—who are mostly Native Alaskans such as the Inuit and Aleut—did not have telephone service. Their villages are small and separated by great distances. The villages are too far apart to lay telephone cable, so communicating with a relative often meant a long journey, perhaps over several hundred miles, and often by dog sled.

Because radio waves could find their way over the rough terrain to nearby towns, rural Alaskans would sometimes broadcast messages to their distant friends and families through a local radio station. They'd send messages out for all to hear. The messages would be about anything from asking for supplies to reminding relatives to take their medication.

The only other communication device that could transmit signals from village to village was shortwave radio. But simply outfitting all rural Alaskans with shortwave radios wouldn't solve the problem. Shortwave radio doesn't always work well in rural Alaska, because of the Aurora Borealis, the Northern Lights, which can interfere with shortwave radio signals.

| Meters | $10^3$ | $10^2$ | $10$ | $1$ | $10^{-1}$ | $10^{-2}$ | $10^{-3}$ | $10^{-4}$ | $10^{-5}$ | $10^{-6}$ | $10^{-7}$ | $10^{-8}$ | $10^{-9}$ | $10^{-10}$ | $10^{-11}$ | $10^{-12}$ |
|---|---|---|---|---|---|---|---|---|---|---|---|---|---|---|---|---|

Radio waves   Microwaves   Infrared   Ultraviolet   X-ray   Gamma ray

**Size of:**

Houses   Orange   Grain of salt   Amoeba   Visible   Protein   Molecules

**Emitted by:**

Radio   Microwave oven   Radar   Person   Light bulb   Medical X-ray device   Radioactive substance

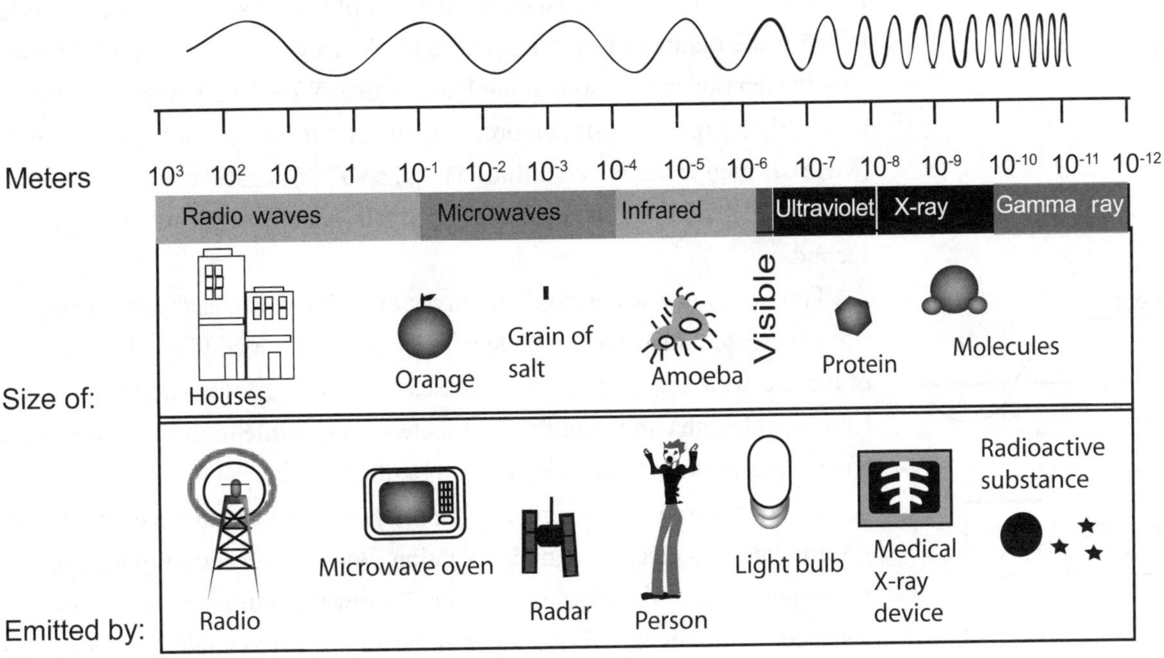

To understand the problem, you have to take a closer look at what radio waves are. Radio waves are a type of electromagnetic radiation. As you can see in the chart above, there are many types of electromagnetic radiation, including visible light, X-rays, microwaves, and gamma rays. Electromagnetic radiation starts at a source, and then travels outward from the source in all directions.

*Electromagnetic radiation* is often described as waves of energy. In the same way that electricity can carry an encoded signal, electromagnetic waves can also carry encoded signals. Electromagnetic radiation is very useful for transmitting information because it travels very fast. All electromagnetic radiation—from radio waves to gamma rays—travels at the speed of light, about 300,000 kilometers per second. And unlike electrical signals, electromagnetic radiation does not require wires. That's why it's ideal for wireless communication systems, such as radio, cell phones, satellites, and Wi-Fi systems.

In the drawing of a radio signal on the next page, you'll see that one *wavelength* is one complete wave, labeled as the distance from the peak of the one wave to the next peak. Radio wavelengths can be the length of a football field or the length of your foot. Radio waves have the longest wavelength of any wave on the spectrum.

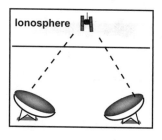

**Wavelength**
is the length of one complete wave.

**Frequency**
is the number of waves per second.

As wavelength decreases, frequency increases.

Radio waves also have the lowest frequency. Frequency refers to the number of complete wave cycles that occur in a unit of time, usually measured in Hertz, which is the number of cycles per second. When you listen to a radio station and hear the announcer say something like, "This is 93.9, The River," the announcer is identifying the radio station broadcasting at a frequency of 93.9 megahertz (MHz). A megahertz is one million Hertz, so 93.9 megahertz means that the transmitter is sending out a radio wave at a frequency of 93,900,000 cycles per second.

Frequency and wavelength are inversely related. So, as the frequency of a wave increases, its wavelength decreases, and vice versa. If you look at the chart of the Electromagnetic Spectrum, you can see that very-low-frequency waves have wavelengths up to hundreds of meters long, while high-frequency waves have wavelengths of only a billionth of a meter!

Frequency and wavelength are important when designing a communications system that uses electromagnetic radiation. Wavelength certainly was an important piece of the puzzle in Alaska. Shortwave radio can travel long distances by bouncing off of a layer of the atmosphere called the *ionosphere* and angling back to Earth. The ionosphere contains many electrically charged particles. If the wavelength of a radio signal is greater than the spacing between charged particles, the radio signal arriving from the surface of the Earth can be reflected, or bounced off the ionosphere and sent back toward the Earth. However, in Alaska, the Aurora Borealis can interfere with this bounce. The Aurora Borealis is a disruption in the ionosphere caused by solar flares, storms on the surface of the sun.

Because these disruptions are unpredictable, shortwave radio was not a dependable solution for providing 24-hour communication in Alaska. Our team looked for another solution. We needed to find a wavelength that would work, but which one? The wavelength had to be small enough and the frequency high enough to be dependable. After researching many possibilities, we decided to use a satellite communication system.

What's different about satellite systems? The satellites we used were located well above the ionosphere, approximately twenty-two thousand miles above sea level. And they operated at a frequency of four to six-gigahertz (GHz)—four to six billion cycles per second—much higher than 30-MHz of the highest shortwave frequency. A higher frequency meant a much shorter wavelength, one that was not disrupted by solar flares. The radio signals sent at these high frequencies pass freely through the ionosphere to the satellite, which relays the signals back to an Earth station in Alaska.

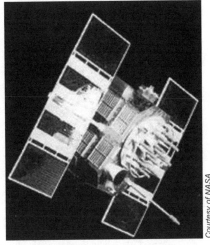
This satellite is used for Global Positioning Systems.

## How a Satellite Phone Call Works

Let's say that a bush pilot named Bill lives in an Alaskan village and is able to use a modern satellite network. Bill wants to call a biologist named Maria, who flies to remote regions of Alaska to observe polar bear populations. Maria lives 150 miles away from Bill in the city of Anchorage. When Bill calls Maria, the sound waves from his voice are encoded by the telephone into electrical signals. The signals are transmitted through telephone wires to an Earthbound transmission station. At the station, the transmitter translates the encoded electrical signal into six-GHz radio waves and attaches a receiving address for the second Earth station. Any type of information may be encoded in the signal. It could be research data, a CNN video stream, or music.

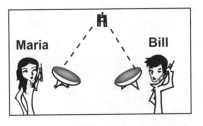

The six-GHz signal is sent to the satellite, which has a receiver that "listens" at that frequency for Earth station transmissions. As soon as the satellite receives the message, the satellite relays or retransmits that signal as a four-GHz signal. A second Earth station in Anchorage receives the signal containing Bill's words and converts the radio signal back into an electrical signal. The signal is sent by telephone line to Maria's office, where her telephone decodes the electrical signal back into sound waves that she can hear. The conversation continues this way in both directions: Bill's Earth station transmits his words at six-GHz, and the satellite sends them back down to Maria's Earth station at four-GHz.

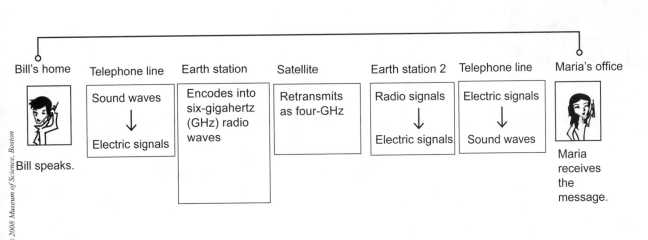

| Bill's home | Telephone line | Earth station | Satellite | Earth station 2 | Telephone line | Maria's office |
|---|---|---|---|---|---|---|
| Bill speaks. | Sound waves ↓ Electric signals | Encodes into six-gigahertz (GHz) radio waves | Retransmits as four-GHz | Radio signals ↓ Electric signals | Electric signals ↓ Sound waves | Maria receives the message. |

## Designing Outside the Box

Using satellites to communicate worked very well in Alaska, because the solution fit the circumstance. Faced with sparse population, long distances, and rough terrain, we needed to look for innovative ways to solve the communications problem.

Our solution solved the problems with providing telephone communications in the region. It also became the foundation on which we built the first Internet in Alaska. In 1987, the University of Alaska connected its fourteen remote campuses across the state using our satellite network. When telephone cables were unavailable, satellite communication links were used for long distances. In some cases, microwave systems moved information over shorter distances where no telephone cables could be laid. All of this was done between campuses in the same fashion as Bill and Maria's phone call.

Putting Alaska's information pipeline into place made many things possible. Doctors in rural areas were able to consult with doctors in cities using video connections. Satellite transmissions and Internet access made it possible for teachers in the cities to teach courses to students in remote villages. In many ways, the combination of wired and wireless communication technologies in Alaska gave us a glimpse of how wireless would later be used in computer networks.

Because of my experience in Alaska, I later advised Australia and Russia on how to improve their networks. I've also lectured on the subject at universities around the world, from South Africa and New Zealand, to Chile, and many more. Radio let me to travel to many unknown foreign lands in a way I never dreamed.

Courtesy of Carnegie Mellon University

To test the Wi-Fi system I developed, I moved my laptop around campus to see if I could stay connected to the Internet the whole time.

## Building a Wireless Network

If we could use radio waves to communicate wirelessly over long distances, it would make sense that we could use them over short distances as well. This idea led to the birth of Wi-Fi. In 1993 I started a project at Carnegie Mellon University in Pittsburgh called Wireless Andrew, which was the first wireless computing network.

Wireless Andrew allows anyone to carry a laptop computer anywhere on campus and connect to the campus network and the Internet. The laptop is equipped with a wireless network card—a transmitter-receiver combination that can send a signal by radio to a nearby access point. An access point is a radio transmitter-receiver that converts the radio waves into electrical signals and sends the signals to the wired part of the network. Access points may be placed anywhere in a room or building and can communicate with nearby computers.

Radio waves have become a very popular way to transmit information. Radio and television stations, cell phone networks, air traffic control systems, cordless telephones, and even garage door openers all use radio waves to communicate. How all of these different systems with millions of different users can all use radio waves without crossing signals very often is one of the beauties of the electromagnetic spectrum. Each device communicates using a specific frequency. You can observe this when you tune your radio in to a specific frequency to pick up a certain radio broadcast.

These technologies allow people to communicate between the most remote regions of our planet. I truly believe they are improving the quality of life for people all over the world by giving them access to medical information, educational resources, business contacts, and a lot more. And making the world a smaller place, at least from my perspective, only brings the adventure home.

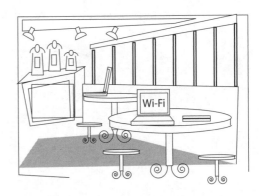

##  What's the Story?

1. When Alex arrived in Alaska in 1970, why didn't people in the Alaskan bush have telecommunications services? How did rural Alaskans communicate over long distances?

2. How did Alex draw on his earlier work in Alaska when developing Wi-Fi technology?

##  Designing with Math and Science

3. Why wouldn't shortwave radio solve the communications problem in rural Alaska? How did satellites solve the problem? Be sure to define the term "wavelength" in your response.

4. What is the frequency of the broadcast by your favorite radio station?

##  Connecting the Dots

5. Draw a communications diagram of a typical Wi-Fi network call. Label the parts with the following terms: sender, receiver, signal, encoder, and decoder. Label where the signal is an electrical signal and where the signal is a radio wave.

6. Some rural Alaskan villages are not on the Alaskan power distribution grid. List a few ways that the towns might power the communications technologies they now use.

## What Do You Think?

7. Using the Internet and the library, find other common communications technologies that use radio waves. List at least three in addition to those mentioned in this chapter.

# 31

## *Sunny Side Up*

### Christine Bordonaro

### Key Concepts
#### from Previous Chapters

- **6** Manufacturing Technologies
- **18** Radiation
- **21** Renewable Energy Source
- **28** Current, Resistance
- **28** Electric Pressure Difference
- **30** AC/DC

Some researchers estimate that in just three days the sun transfers more energy to Earth than the energy in all the fossil fuels on the planet. That's a lot of energy! By harnessing even a small percentage of it, we could start to solve some of the health and environmental problems associated with using fossil fuels as our primary source of energy.

Finding ways to capture that energy cost effectively is the major goal of my work. I'm Christine Bordonaro, and my company, Evergreen Solar, makes solar panels to generate electric power using the energy from sunlight. The solar panels we use today provide enough electricity to power calculators, schools, cars, and even satellites in space. We're working to make them more useful by increasing their efficiency and decreasing their cost.

*Courtesy of Pacific Northwest National Laboratory*

Wind and hydroelectric power are two renewable energy sources. A hydroelectric dam harnesses the energy in falling water to turn a turbine and generate electricity.

I'm excited to share my experiences as an engineer because, when I was growing up, I had no way of finding out what engineers did. As a high school student in Rochester, New York, I was good at math and science. My teachers encouraged me to study engineering in college. But I didn't really know what engineering was or what engineers did until I was well on my way to becoming one.

In college, I studied mechanical engineering. The courses I took covered a wide range of topics including design, construction, and product development. In graduate school, I got interested in materials science, which studies the characteristics and uses of the various materials. I was fascinated how two materials made up of the same basic substances can have totally different properties. I studied polymers—or plastics—and eventually got a Masters Degree and a Ph.D. from Rensselaer Polytechnic Institute.

When I learned about a job opening at Evergreen Solar I became excited. This job would let me develop solar technologies that could help solve some very serious environmental and public health problems. As a renewable energy source, the sun can give us as much solar energy as we want. Unlike coal or oil, there is a constant self-replenishing source: the sun!

Solar energy offers other benefits too. For one, using solar energy allows *decentralized electrical generation.* That means that anyone anywhere can put a solar panel in a sunny spot, plug it in, and get power. Solar panels generate electricity on the spot. No power grid required!

In a *centralized electrical generation* system, large volumes of fossil fuels are mined, stored, and transported to power stations that generate electricity, which is distributed across the power grid. Solar power, on the other hand, does not require storing, transporting, and burning fossil fuels for electrical power. And very little solar power gets "lost" through miles and miles of wire on the grid.

# What Is Solar Energy?

The energy in sunlight originates at the sun's center. The sun, made mostly of hydrogen, has a very strong gravitational field, strong enough to hold the planets of our solar system in orbit. At the sun's core, the pressure is so huge that the temperature reaches about 14 million degrees Celsius, which results in a nuclear reaction called fusion. Unlike a nuclear reactor that generates heat by splitting atoms in a process called fission, a star, like the sun, uses the generated heat to fuse the atoms of hydrogen into helium. This process releases a tremendous amount of energy that radiates from the sun in all directions.

*Radiation* is the energy transmitted in all directions from a source in the form of waves and rays. Whether it's the sound waves from your headphones, heat from a stove, or the light from the sun, you live with radiation every day. When the radiation from the sun reaches the Earth, much of the energy warms the atmosphere, raising the Earth's temperature.

In *active solar technologies,* sunlight is used to warm a fluid, such as water, which is pumped to a storage tank, called a solar collector. The stored hot fluid can then be used for space heating or as a hot water supply. Because these systems require pumps to move the fluid around, they are referred to as active solar technologies.

*Passive solar technologies* are designed to use the remaining energy mostly for heat or light. Buildings designed with passive technologies often have large south-facing windows, allowing plenty of sunlight to pour in. Some buildings are made from materials that readily absorb energy from the sun. The floors and walls made from concrete, brick, and other materials absorb the sun's energy by heating up during the day. At night, the stored energy radiates to its surroundings.

*Radiation* ⌇↗
is the energy transmitted in all directions from a source in the form of waves and rays.

Courtesy of Stefano Paltera/Solar Decathlon

Here at Evergreen Solar, we harness the energy in sunlight in a different way altogether. We make ***photovoltaic,*** or PV, cells. PV cells transfer the energy in light (photo) into electricity (voltaic).

Many PV cells are made with silicon, which is found in sand. And sand is one of the most abundant elements on Earth. Pure silicon itself is not a very good conductor, so it is mixed with some other materials that increase its conductivity. In a manufacturing process called "doping," we add phosphorus to one side of the PV cell, while the other side is doped with boron. When the cell is exposed to light, a greater charge builds up on the side of the cell that is doped with phosphorus. The two sides of the cell can then be connected into a circuit.

When sunlight strikes the cell, the difference in charge on the two sides creates an electric pressure difference or voltage. Charge flows in a current from the phosphorus-doped side of the cell through the circuit to the boron-doped side of the cell. While each cell can produce only a small current, by connecting PV cells together, we can construct solar panels that can produce usable power.

**A Photovoltaic Cell**

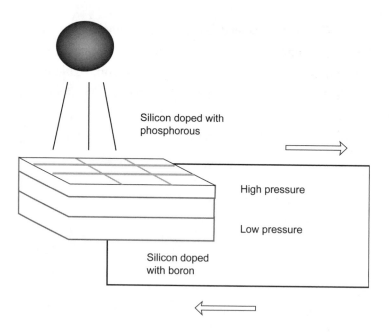

Silicon doped with phosphorous

High pressure

Low pressure

Silicon doped with boron

## In the Dark

Whenever I describe to my friends how solar cells work, they always ask the same question: "What happens at night when there is not enough light to create a current?" It's a good question. You would never want to install solar panels in your home if you thought you couldn't turn on lights or take a warm shower at night, would you? But there's no getting around the fact that PV cells need light to generate electricity. Some people purchase expensive batteries that store extra electrical power generated by the panels during the day, which powers their homes at night.

More often, people keep their homes connected to the distribution grid, so they can buy electricity from the grid at night. During the day, their solar panels often generate more electricity than they need and the excess electricity is fed back into the grid. Most power companies will even buy the electricity that a homeowner supplies to the grid. In a sense, these homes act like small power plants in daylight hours.

## Why Not Go Solar?

Given that solar panels can help the environment and bring in a little extra income, why doesn't everyone have them? Well, there are a few problems associated with PV technology that engineers have yet to truly solve, but we're getting closer. To start with, solar cells need to be more efficient. A solar cell only transfers about 15 percent of the radiation that hits it into electricity. Each solar panel that has two strings of 36 solar cells generates about 100 Watts of electricity—enough electrical energy to power one bright light bulb. To supply electricity to an entire house, you need many solar panels connected together. For this reason, it's critical for PV cells to be as efficient as possible.

One type of technology that improves efficiency allows the solar cells to track the sun moving across the sky much the way a sunflower does. This maximizes the amount of light that hits a cell and the amount of electricity that each panel can produce. Evergreen is also working to create anti-reflective coatings for solar panels that will allow more sunlight to pass into the cell instead of being reflected from the panel's surface.

Many people find the costs of buying and installing solar panels too high. While the initial installation costs are high, over the life of the PV panels, homeowners can save enough on electrical bills to make up most or all of the costs. States such as California, New Jersey, and Maryland now offer to pay up to 70% of the installation fees as an incentive for residents to switch to solar power. Some European countries offer even larger financial incentives to go solar. This may explain why Germany produces twice as much electric power using solar energy than the United States, while its population is just over a quarter of the size. It also may explain why Evergreen sells a lot of solar panels to Germany.

At Evergreen Solar, we're optimizing our manufacturing systems to bring the costs of solar panels down so that more people—in the United States and abroad—find them affordable. The way we make our silicon cells, for instance, reduces costs. Most companies take a block of silicon and cut it. If you have ever used a saw to cut anything, you know that a small strip of the material as wide as the thickness of the saw turns into sawdust. The same is true for cutting silicon. Cutting a thin slice of silicon from a block results in silicon dust on the floor. We warm our silicon until it melts, then pull it upward between two strings. This process saves us money because we don't waste very much silicon.

I believe that using solar energy will be commonplace in the United States one day. But before that can happen, we have to keep working on ways to improve PV cells. I'm proud to be a part of that effort!

## What's the Story?

1. Why is it beneficial to use renewable energy sources?

2. Why does Christine say that solar technologies represent decentralized power generation? What are the advantages of this type of power generation?

3. How do homes powered by PV panels get power at night?

## Designing with Math and Science

4. Christine says that solar panels are only about 15 percent efficient. What are the inputs and outputs of the solar panel system that Christine is using to determine efficiency?

5. What is radiation?

## Connecting the Dots

6. What are some differences between how solar panels generate electricity and how a generator in a coal-fired power plant generates electricity?

## What Do You Think?

7. Imagine that you've just been hired by the marketing department of Evergreen Solar. Your job is to create an advertisement for a national magazine that will get more people interested in solar panels despite the costs of installing them. Your ad must describe how the benefits of solar outweigh the installation costs. Use drawings and text to describe what your ad would be like.

# 32

## *Cape Wind*

### Jim Gordon

*Courtesy of Jim Gordon*

One of the windiest places in America is near the coast of Massachusetts, near Cape Cod and the neighboring islands of Martha's Vineyard and Nantucket. Having one of the fastest-growing populations in the New England, its electric power demand continues to soar. To help satisfy this growing demand, my company wants to harness the energy of all of that wind. We plan to build an offshore "wind farm" of 130 giant windmills that will provide electricity for the area. But, before we can start building, we have to convince people that a wind farm is a good idea. I'm Jim Gordon, president of Energy Management, Inc., and my company has spent almost thirty years pioneering new directions in electricity generation. We've faced hurdles to every single one of our projects during that time, but we've always been successful. We plan to make this project a success as well.

## Selling Technology

When I was in college, in 1973, the United States faced an energy crisis. Israel and Egypt were at war. The Organization of Petroleum Exporting Countries (OPEC), an international group of countries that includes Saudi Arabia, Kuwait, the United Arab Emirates, and several other nations decided it would no longer export oil to countries supporting Israel. Because we were an ally to Israel, the OPEC countries banned the sale of oil to the U.S. This oil embargo caused a serious oil shortage. With oil in short supply, its price began to skyrocket. Because we burn oil to power our factories and run our vehicles, the cost of transportation, goods, and services soared as well. The higher prices severely damaged our economy.

At the time, it seemed to me that if we could reduce how much oil we use, our economy would not be as vulnerable to such shortages. So I started a company to help factories cut costs by reducing fuel use. Over a ten-year period, from 1975 to 1985, my company developed systems that successfully improved the efficiency of oil-fired power plants.

## Building Power Plants

When oil prices fell in the mid-1980s, we decided to start building our own power plants. At the time, power plants in New England used oil, coal, nuclear energy, and flowing water to produce electricity. Not one plant used natural gas, even though emissions from burning natural gas are much less toxic than using coal or oil. We thought our natural gas plants could be profitable and at the same time reduce harmful emissions. So we started building natural gas power plants.

Using new technologies, we constructed six "combined cycle" gas plants. Unlike a typical power plant, our plants use the leftover hot gases that are usually exhausted into the atmosphere. The hot exhaust gas from one combustion chamber is piped to an additional generator to produce even more electricity. The efficiency of a combined cycle plant—the amount of electricity generated for a given amount of gas—can be double that of a standard gas plant. One of our early plants was located near a paper mill and another near a food processing plant. We sold them the leftover steam, which they used in their industrial processes. This boosted their efficiency and ours, because they didn't have to make their own steam. This type of plant is usually called a "cogeneration" plant, which means it produces both heat and electricity.

*Engineering the Future: Science, Technology, and the Design Process*

With experience, we further improved the efficiency of our plants and even their production capacity. Our first gas plant produced a peak of 40 megawatts (MW) of power, which is enough to power around 40,000 homes. Our last two plants each produced 265 MW. Other companies got into the game, and by the late 1990s almost half of New England's electricity came from burning natural gas.

## Why Wind?

In 1999 we started focusing on what we believe is the next direction of energy development in New England: renewable energy. *Renewable energy* refers to energy sources that renew themselves quickly, such as wind, geothermal, or hydroelectric power. After investigating the technologies currently available, our company determined that wind power was the best option.

We needed to find the best site to develop a wind project. Unlike oil, coal, and natural gas, wind cannot be transported. You have to capture the wind where it is. We spent one year looking all over New England. We discovered a very windy place in the coastal waters of Nantucket Sound. The Sound is shallow enough for building the towers and close enough to shore to run electric cables easily. We're convinced that Nantucket Sound is a great place to develop America's first offshore wind farm.

## The Benefits of Wind

In addition to providing electricity, building wind farms could help in fixing our air pollution problems. The American Lung Association has documented that the area has the worst air quality in Massachusetts. The Cape Wind project will provide 75 percent of the area's electrical needs with zero pollution.

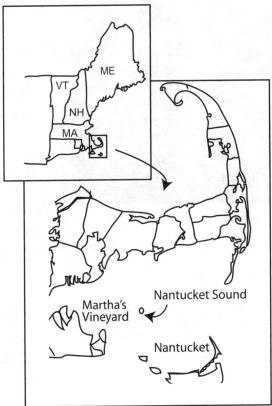

The proposed site for Cape Wind in Horseshoe Shoal, Nantucket Sound

An offshore wind turbine

Our wind farm will have 130 wind turbines, each situated about one-half-mile apart. The towers, from the surface of the water to the center of the blades, will be 247 feet tall, with blades approximately 171 feet long. The base of the towers will be 16 feet in diameter. Each wind turbine will be supported by a hollow steel pipe that will be driven 80 feet into the sandy seabed. The rotating blades spin an electrical generator inside the head of the turbine. Electric cables, embedded on the ocean floor, will connect the turbines to the distribution grid. The wind farm will be capable of producing a maximum of 420 MW in a strong wind, the peak electric demand of the Cape and Islands. Based on our calculations of the average wind speed, we expect to provide approximately 170 MW of the region's average demand of 230 MW. Even with a small breeze, the electricity from the wind farm will be added to the grid.

## The Impact

Some of our opponents complain that the wind farm will cause environmental damage, endangering birds and marine life. Turbines may disrupt bird migration patterns, or birds may fly into the turning blades. We believe that the turbines will be safe for birds, because the towers are designed so that birds cannot nest on them or get caught in wires. And the blades on the turbines rotate slowly, presenting little harm to flying birds.

Others are concerned that Cape Wind will disrupt marine life, fishing, and boating. We're confident that our state-of-the-art construction technologies will minimize disruption to the seabed. The foundations of the turbines will even act as artificial reefs that attract fish. And with the turbines spaced one-third to one-half mile apart, it will be easy for both fishing and recreational boats to get around.

*Engineering the Future: Science, Technology, and the Design Process*

You don't have to take my word about the environmental impact of Cape Wind. The United States Army Corps of Engineers has led a team of 17 federal, state, and regional agencies in a full, comprehensive, and rigorous permitting review. That review indicates that there will be a minimal negative environmental impact.

Yet there are people, including an opposition group called the Alliance to Protect Nantucket Sound, who have publicly stated that they don't want this wind farm. They don't want to look at the wind turbines, even though they will be located five miles away from the closest beach. People using the beach will see what looks like tiny sailing masts on the horizon. Still others think that property values and tourism will be affected, but in Denmark, property values and tourism have risen in the communities near an offshore wind farm.

## Energy Future

If you talk to my opponents, they will tell you, "We support renewable energy—just not here." Well, if everybody said that, we wouldn't have renewable energy sources anywhere! I think that we all have the responsibility of supporting renewable energy technologies—even if they are in our own backyards.

I've spent most of my career helping to reduce fuel consumption, pollutant emissions, and developing the cleanest power facilities in New England. What motivates me is the ability to push new technologies to the limit to boost productivity and cost competitiveness. Given the choice, I believe that informed citizens would prefer to purchase clean energy, which will reduce pollution and increase their health and the health of their children.

## What's the Story?

1. Why does Jim want to build a wind power plant off of the coast of Nantucket?

2. Describe two features that increase plant efficiency in the combined cycle power plants that Jim developed.

## Designing with Math and Science

3. Using what you know about turbines, explain with words and drawings how a wind turbine generates electricity.

## Connecting the Dots

4. What advantages does wind power generation have over coal-fired power plants? What are the disadvantages?

## What Do You Think?

5. Use the library and the Internet to research other types of renewable energy sources.

6. Based on what you know about electricity generation, how might falling water, found in a waterfall or a stream flowing downhill, be used to generate electricity?

# Glossary

**active solar heating** – Systems that use energy from the sun to warm up fluids, which are pumped from collectors to storage tanks and then circulated.

**active solar technologies** – Technologies that use pumps or other mechanical methods to move fluids heated by solar energy.

**alternating current (AC)** – Electric current that reverses direction, usually many times per second. Most electrical generators produce alternating current.

**ampere (amp)** – The unit of measurement for current.

**analog** – Continuous and variable electrical waves that represent an infinite number of values.

**analog signal** – A continuous electrical signal in the form of waves that varies as the source of the information varies.

**assembly** – The stage of production in which components are put together into an end product.

**battery** – A device that stores energy and makes it available in an electrical form.

**biodiesel** – A fuel made from vegetable oil such as corn and soybean oil that can be used to power a diesel engine.

**boiler** – A closed vessel in which water or other fluid is heated under pressure to create steam.

**building codes** – Community ordinances that govern how a building can be constructed or modified. Codes regulate the structural, electrical, plumbing, and fire safety design.

**building inspector** – A government employee that enforces the country, state, and city building codes and laws.

**buoyant force** – The upward force on an object immersed in a fluid.

**cantilever** – A part of a structure that extends beyond its support structure.

**casting** – A process by which a material is introduced into a mold while it is liquid and allowed to solidify in the shape of the mold, usually metal or ceramic.

**centralized electrical generation** – Systems that use large power stations to generate electricity, which is distributed through an electrical power grid.

**charge** – The amount of electricity carried by a body.

**chemical reaction** – A process that breaks apart molecules; the atoms are then rearranged into new molecules. When molecules break apart, they release energy, usually in the form of heat and light.

**closed system** – A system in which the working fluid remains inside the engine.

**combustion chamber** – The part of an engine in which fuel is burned. In a rocket, liquid hydrogen and liquid oxygen are pumped into the combustion chamber, where they combine and burn explosively.

**composite materials** – Materials composed of at least two other materials. The properties of a composite are more desirable than the properties of its individual components.

**compressible** – Capable of being compressed or made more compact. Compressible fluids are usually gases such as air that occupy a smaller volume under pressure.

**compression** – The process that occurs when an object is pressed together.

**conditioning** – Any process that changes the properties of a material using heat, chemicals, or mechanical force.

**conductor** – A material through which energy passes easily. Most metals are good conductors of thermal and electrical energy.

**constraints** – A limitation to be considered in designing and developing technology.

**convection** – Energy transfer due to fluid motion.

**cosmic rays** – High-energy radiation that originates beyond Earth.

**criteria** – Desired features.

**current** – The flow of electricity through a conductor, measured in amperes.

**dead load** – The load or weight of a structure itself. In a bridge, the steel, concrete, and other materials used to create the supporting structure and the roadway.

**decentralized electrical generation** – Use of relatively small systems to generate electricity located at or near point of use, which does not use distribution grids.

**decimal system** – A base 10 system, a numeric system that uses ten digits.

**digital** – A method of storing information as a string of binary digits, or ones and zeros.

**digital signal** – An electrical signal consisting of discrete on and off pulses.

**direct current (DC)** – Electricity that flows through a conductor in one direction.

**durable goods** – Goods that have a life span of three or more years, such as cars, hand tools, ovens, and furniture.

**efficiency** – The measure of energy inputs with respect to the useful outputs of a system. In an ideal system that is 100 percent efficient, the useful outputs are equal to the inputs.

**elastic deformation** – A temporary change that occurs to a material after being subjected to stress below its elastic limit.

**elastic limit** – The maximum stress a material can experience and return to its original shape when the stress is removed.

**electric circuit** – The path followed by an electrical charge from a power source (generator or battery), through an electrical system, then returning to the source.

**electricity** – The electrical charge flowing in wires.

**electron** – A negatively charged particle of an atom that orbits the nucleus.

**electronics** – Devices used to control and transform electricity to accomplish tasks such as transistors, integrated circuits (ICs), and computers.

**elements** – Substances that have only one kind of atom.

**elevation drawing** – An orthographic 2-D projection drawing of the above-ground portion of a structure.

**encode** – The process of converting or translating information into electric signals.

**engine** – A system that converts the thermal energy created by temperature differences to mechanical work.

**engineer** – Person who creates, designs, develops, or improves technologies to meet human needs or wants.

**engineering design process** – A guide used by engineers to create, invent, and develop technologies.

**ergonomics** – The study of how people interact with machines and systems in designed environments in order to improve product design.

**failure point** – The point at which a material breaks or fractures.

**feedback** – Process information that the system uses to make adjustments during manufacturing.

**finishing** – Any final treatment done to the surface of a product to make the product more attractive to a consumer.

**fission** – The splitting apart of an atom's nucleus, releasing a large amount of heat energy.

**fluid** – A substance that flows easily, such as a liquid or a gas.

**fluid pressure difference** – The pressure difference between fluids created by an obstruction.

**footprint** – The area contained within the perimeter of the building, usually defined by its foundation.

**forming** – The use of pressure or force to shape a material.

**foundation** – A structure that transmits loads from a building to the underlying ground.

**frequency** – The number of complete wave cycles that occur in a unit of time, usually measured in hertz.

**fusion** – The process that creates heavier atoms from lighter ones as a result of extremely high temperatures.

**goal** – The defined or desired result of a designed system.

**grid** – The electrical distribution network of power stations, distribution stations, and wiring that delivers electrical power to users.

**heating** – The increase in temperature resulting from energy crossing a system boundary.

**hertz (Hz)** – The unit of measure of one complete wave cycle per second.

**hydraulic system** – A system that uses liquid to transmit power by taking advantage of fluid characteristics and pressure changes.

**incompressible** – Not subject to being pressed together or changes in volume under pressure.

**innovation** – The invention of a new device or system, based on existing technologies.

**inputs** – Everything that goes into the system in order to achieve the desired goal.

**insulator** – A material through which energy does not flow well.

**ionosphere** – Electrified region of the upper atmosphere where fairly large concentrations of ions and free electrons exist.

**isometric projection** – A representation of a 3-D shape in two dimensions. All vertical lines are drawn vertically, but all horizontal lines are drawn at 30 degrees to the horizontal.

**Law of Conservation of Energy** – The energy inputs of a system will always equal the energy outputs, regardless of the processes.

**Law of Conservation of Mass** – The mass of the inputs to a system will always be the same as the mass of the outputs from a system, regardless of the processes involved.

**live load** – The force applied to a structure from materials that are not a part of the structure, such as cars, people, furniture, snow, and wind.

**linear** – Relationship between input and output in which the output varies in direct proportion to the input.

**load** – The total weight subjected on a structure.

In electricity, a device that uses the energy supplied by the moving charge to do work, such as a motor or a light bulb.

**metric system** – A system of measurements in which all of the units are based on multiples of ten.

**microenterprise** – A small business that can be run by an individual or a family.

**mold** – A shaped container into which a substance is poured and left to solidify.

**molding** – The forming of a material into a prescribed shape and size, usually by pouring the heated material such as plastic into a mold.

**molecule** – The smallest particle of a material that has all the chemical properties of that material.

**natural materials** – Raw materials produced by nature, such as leather, cotton, gold, and plants.

**neutron** – Particle of the nucleus of an atom that has no charge.

**New Urbanism** – An urban design movement that began in the late 1980s and early 1990s, with the aim to reform how our cities grow and to rebuild our regions, cities, towns, and villages. New Urbanism promotes neighborhoods that are walkable, and include a diverse range of places to live, work, shop, and relax.

**non-durable goods** – Manufactured items that usually last only a very short time and are disposable.

**non-linear** – Relationship between input and output in which the output is not proportional to the input.

**nozzle** – In a rocket, a small opening from which the hot gases from burning fuels escapes.

**nuclear reaction** – A process that changes the atoms of a substance, which results in the release of energy.

**nucleus** – A tiny, dense bail of matter at the center of an atom.

**oblique drawing** – A representation of an object in which the front side of the object appears flat in the picture plane and the edges of the object are at a 45-degree angle to the horizontal lines of the front side.

**ohm** – The unit of measurement for resistance in an electrical circuit.

**Ohm's Law** – The mathematical relationship between voltage difference ($\Delta V$), current (I), and resistance (R), defined by the equation $\Delta V = IR$.

**optimize** – To increase the efficiency or effectiveness of a process as much as possible.

**orthographic projection** – A two-dimensional (2-D), or flat, representation of a 3-D object using views of each side of the object.

**outputs** – Everything produced by the process.

**parallel circuit** – An electrical circuit in which the current branches before each component.

**passive solar heating** – Refers to designing a home to take advantage of sunlight for heating.

**patent** – A document issued by the government that gives an inventor the sole right to make, distribute, or sell a particular invention for a certain number of years.

**patent research** – Examination of old patents to learn about how other engineers developed related technologies.

**period** – In construction, the time it takes for a structure to complete one full cycle by swinging back and forth due to an outside force.

**perspective drawing** – A realistic 2-D representation of a 3-D object in which parallel lines that recede from the viewer are drawn so they seem to converge at a vanishing point in the distance.

**photovoltaic (PV) cell** – A material made from two layers of different materials that can produce an electric current from light energy.

**plan drawing** – An orthographic projection, showing the top-down view of the structure. The plan drawing communicates the floor plan of the structure.

**plastic deformation** – A permanent change in the shape of a material resulting from stress levels at or above the elastic limit.

**power** – The amount of energy transferred in a given amount of time.

**pressure** – The force exerted per unit area, often used to describe the force exerted by a contained fluid.

**pressure difference** – The difference in pressure between substances created by an obstruction.

**primary processing** – The first step in transforming raw materials into useful materials.

**proton** – A particle of the nucleus of an atom with a positive charge.

**prototype** – A full-scale working model that tests whether a technology meets the requirements.

**radiation** – The energy transmitted in all directions from a source in the form of waves and rays.

**raw materials** – The natural, unrefined resources of the Earth.

**renewable energy source** – An energy source that is naturally replenished in a short amount of time.

**resistance** – A measure of the amount of opposition to forward movement. In electricity, the amount of opposition to the flow of an electric current. It is measured in ohms ($\Omega$).

**resistors** – Components that have a resistance to electric current that never changes.

**shear** – The force that results in the deformation of an object in which its parallel planes remain parallel but move past one another.

**short circuit** – An accidental lower-resistance connection that bypasses the load or the resistance in a circuit.

**scale** – The ratio of the size of the drawing of an object to the size of the actual object.

**scientists** – People who observe and investigate how the natural world functions and develop explanations for why things happen.

**separating** – A process that removes unwanted materials.

**series circuit** – An electrical circuit in which current passes through components one after the other in a chain.

**solar flares** – Storms on the surface of the sun, which results in increases in electromagnetic radiation.

**source** – In electricity, the supplier of the energy carried by the moving charge.

**strain** – A measure of the amount a material deforms due to stress as compared with its original size.

**strength** – A measure of the stress a material can support without failing or deforming.

**stress** – The measure of the force that resists a change in the volume or shape of a material measured in units of force per area.

**sustainable development** – The process of directing the growth of a city so that it meets the needs of current residents without compromising the needs of future residents.

**synthetic material** – A substance that is formulated or manufactured by a chemical process or by a process that chemically changes a substance.

**system** – A group of parts that work together to achieve a specific goal.

**technology** – Anything that people do to change the natural world to suit human needs and wants.

**temperature** – The measure of the concentration of thermal energy in a substance.

**tension** – The force that occurs when the ends of an object are pulled away from its center.

**thermal expansion** – The increase in size of a material as a result of an increase in its temperature due to heat.

**thermal mass** – A mass, such as concrete, that absorbs and stores energy.

**thrust** – The forward force produced in reaction to the gases escaping rearward from a jet or rocket engine.

**torsion** – A twisting force that results when one side of an object moves relative to the other side.

**truss** – A triangular arrangement of structural members that increases a structure's rigidity.

**uranium** – The heaviest element normally found in nature. The principal fuel material used in today's nuclear reactors, uranium-235.

**urban sprawl** – A term that describes the rapid expansion of a city toward low-density surrounding areas.

**volt** – The measure of pressure difference in an electric circuit.

**voltage** – The electric pressure difference in an electric circuit.

**watt** – The measure of power in an electric circuit, calculated as the product of current and voltage.

**wavelength** – The distance of one complete wave of electromagnetic radiation, usually measured from peak to peak of the wave.

**work** – The energy transferred through a system that causes an object to move.

**working fluid** – The liquid contained within a hydraulic system, usually oil or water.

**zoning laws** – Regulations that govern how land and the structures on them can be used. Zoning laws dictate the height, distance from other structures, and a variety of other restrictions.

# Unit Conversions

## Length

1 inch = 2.54 centimeters
1 foot = 0.3048 meters
1 yard = 3 feet
1 meter = 39.4 inches
1 mile = 5,280 feet = 1.61 kilometer
1 kilometer = 0.6121 miles

## Units of Area

1 square inch = 6.45 square centimeters
1 square foot = 929 square centimeters
1 acre = 43,560 square feet

## Units of Volume

1 gallon (U.S.) = 231 cubic inches
1 gallon = 3.79 liters
1 cubic inch = 16.4 cubic centimeters
1 liter = 1,000 cubic centimeters

## Force and Mass

1 ounce = 28.3 grams
1 pound = 16 ounces
1 kilogram = 2.205 pounds
1 Newton = 0.225 pounds

## Energy and Work

1 joule = $9.48 \times 10^{-4}$ BTUs
1 calorie = 4.1868 joules
1 BTU = 1,055 joules = $2.93 \times 10^{-4}$ kilowatt-hour
1 kilowatt-hour = $3.60 \times 10^{6}$ joules = 3,412 BTUs

## Pressure

1 atm = 14.7 PSI = 101,325 Pascal
1 PSI (Pounds per Square Inch) = 6,894.76 Pascal = 0.068 atm

Some teachers will ask you to convert from the English system of units to the metric system, which is used in most countries by most scientists. To do so, you can use these unit conversion factors. Keep in mind that most factors are approximations. More precise values can be found on the internet.